PATTERNS
IN CRYSTALS

PATTERNS
IN CRYSTALS

Noel F. Kennon

Department of Metallurgy
The University of Wollongong, Australia

JOHN WILEY & SONS
Chichester · New York · Brisbane · Toronto

Library of Congress Cataloging in Publication Data:

Kennon, Noel F.
    Patterns in crystals.

    Includes index.
    1. Crystals. I. Title.
QD921.K52   548'.81   78-4531

ISBN 0 471 99748 x (Cloth)
ISBN 0 471 99652 1 (Paper)

Typeset in IBM Press Roman by
Preface Ltd, Salisbury, Wilts
Printed in Great Britain by
Unwin Brothers Ltd,
The Gresham Press, Old Woking, Surrey.

To Hilda who waged and finally won her own private battle with these matters

Contents

Preface ix
Chapter 1.   Plane Patterns 1
Chapter 2.   Plane Lattices 10
Chapter 3.   The Unit Cell of a Plane Lattice 17
Chapter 4.   Simple Symmetry 27
Chapter 5.   Fractional Coordinates 41
Chapter 6.   Indices in Plane Lattices 46
Chapter 7.   The Line Spacing 57
Chapter 8.   Crystals 60
Chapter 9.   Space Lattices 66
Chapter 10. Macroscopic Symmetry 75
Chapter 11. Point Groups 83
Chapter 12. Crystal Systems 88
Chapter 13. The Unit Cell of a Crystal 92
Chapter 14. Bravais Lattices 97
Chapter 15. Crystal Structures 118
Chapter 16. Microscopic Symmetry 129
Chapter 17. Space Groups 135
Chapter 18. Defects in Crystals 138
Chapter 19. Miller Indices 146
Chapter 20. Miller–Bravais Indices 164
Chapter 21. The d-Spacing 170
Chapter 22. Crystals and X-Rays 180
Index 195

Preface

Crystals and the search for an understanding of them have fascinated mankind ever since the finding of prisms of quartz high in the European Alps many thousands of years ago. In fact the word CRYSTAL is derived from the Greek κρυσταλλος meaning 'ice' or 'frozen water', for it was mistakenly believed that these unusual stones were formed from water by the intense cold of the lofty passes where they occurred.

The word CRYSTAL was used only in reference to the icy transparency and purity of quartz until about the 17th century, but then the meaning gradually expanded to refer to other stones (minerals) also occurring naturally with regular shapes bounded by plane faces. Today the word is used in a totally different way and it is with the concepts involved in the current usage that this book is concerned.

Many familiar solids are crystals – the tiny grains of sugar and table salt, the adamantine diamond, the brilliant ruby, emerald, sapphire and other gemstones, the prisms of quartz, the flakes of mica, the minerals of many kinds, the salts such as copper sulphate and potash alum grown from saturated solutions, the delicate snowflake, and so on. These particular solids are easily recognized as crystals because the natural shape is often distinctly regular with flat faces and straight edges.

Originally, the science of crystals – CRYSTALLOGRAPHY – was concerned only to measure the shapes of the naturally occurring minerals and to use the measurements to classify them. This situation existed until the turn of the present century when the clues which led ultimately to an understanding of the origin of the distinctive shapes were discovered and the science evolved into the study of these origins and the associated properties.

It is now known that the regular external shape of any crystal is merely a manifestation of regular order in the three-dimensional arrangement of the component atoms or molecules. The regularity, or periodicity of the arrangement is the most important, the most basic, and the most characteristic feature of any crystal. It is the regular internal arrangement that generates the regular external shape of a crystal that grows freely, slowly and without impediment as occurs during the formation of various salts from saturated solutions, or during the deposition of many naturally occurring minerals.

However, if a crystal cannot grow freely the shape is usually irregular, being determined by the environmental constraints within which it develops. For example, during the solidification of a metal, large numbers of crystals form simultaneously and grow competitively to produce irregularly shaped grains interlocked together. In much the same way granite, basalt, and the other igneous rocks occur as many interlocking, irregular crystal grains. Similar structures develop in the sedimentary and metamorphic rocks, in most minerals, in building bricks and mortar, in ceramics, in chemicals, and in a host of other metallic and non-metallic materials.

All solids which are composed of crystals, whether one or more, whether regularly or irregularly shaped, are termed CRYSTALLINE and the characteristic feature of such solids relates solely to the internal periodic arrangement of atoms. Thus the size and external shape are completely irrelevant, being determined only by the accidental conditions that prevailed at the time of formation.

An understanding of crystals, of crystal properties, and of crystal structures is fundamental to many scientific studies at all levels of higher education. The concepts involved in this understanding specifically concern the geometry of the periodic regularity of the arrangements of atoms that characterize the crystalline state. To reach this understanding it is necessary to appreciate that the geometry is actually the geometry of three-dimensional patterns, since a crystal is nothing more nor less than a pattern of atoms in the three dimensions of space. The geometry of such patterns raises difficulties of visualization for it is far from easy to create mental images of complex, three-dimensional objects without considerable practice.

It is far easier to think in two dimensions, to create images, and to picture shapes. A two-dimensional pattern is easily visualized, is easily drawn on paper for detailed study, is easily analysed, and so, for these reasons, the geometry of patterns will first be analysed for the two-dimensional case. The analysis will be developed in terms of a series of CONCEPTS and DEFINITIONS which will later be applied to the more conceptually difficult three-dimensional patterns. Finally the three-dimensional patterns will be related to the arrays of atoms in real crystals and to the ways in which these arrays can be measured.

Since you have opened this book and have read so far, you must have some interest in crystallography. Perhaps you are a geologist, mineralogist, gemmologist, or lapidary interested in crystals as natural phenomena. Or else you might be a materials scientist, a physicist, a chemist, a ceramicist, an engineer, or a metallurgist interested in the relationships between crystals and the properties of solids. Alternatively, you could be an educator seeking to determine whether this book has value for the courses you provide, or a student reading here because it has been suggested that you do so. Whether you are any of these, or someone else again, this book has been written to try to give a little insight into the character of crystals and so enlighten the many other works so readily available but which deal with the subject in a more advanced way.

NOEL KENNON
Wollongong, 1978

Chapter 1

Plane Patterns

What is a pattern? How can it be described? What are the component parts? How can the component parts be specified? What are the important properties?

These are a few of the many questions that can be asked about patterns of all kinds, but particularly about patterns in two dimensions and patterns in three dimensions. This book is far too elementary for readers who can properly answer these questions as it has been prepared for students about to engage in a first scientific enquiry into crystallography and do not know how to go about finding the answers to the questions they would like to ask. Readers who cannot answer the questions will find that as the two-dimensional plane pattern is examined progressively those answers will begin to come, and to come easily, and with them will develop the level of understanding that will open the way to an appreciation of the crystalline state later on.

Two-dimensional patterns are quite common, occurring on curtain materials, on dress fabrics, on carpets and floor coverings, on gift wrapping paper, in brickwork and trellises, and a host of other places. It is instructive to look about the home, the shops, along the streets, in places of education and employment, everywhere, for other examples to see how widely these patterns do occur in everyday living.

A simple two-dimensional pattern is shown in Figure 1. Careful examination of this pattern will reveal that it has a certain repetitive character, and it is from this repetitiveness that the fundamental nature of patterns arises. Look closely and it will be discovered that the pattern is constructed from two separate ingredients; it is these ingredients that have to be explored in considerable detail to achieve the level of appreciation required to answer the questions posed at the beginning of this chapter.

The first ingredient is the basic unit of the pattern. This basic unit is called the MOTIF, which, for the pattern in Figure 1, is

Secondly, there is the system called the SCHEME OF REPETITION, whereby the motif is repeated over and over to produce the pattern.

Since there are two ingredients of a plane pattern, and two ingredients only, all that is needed to make a pattern is one of each, a MOTIF and a SCHEME OF REPETITION. It follows that any existing pattern can be changed by simply

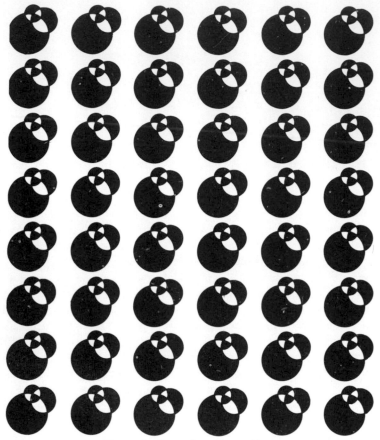

Figure 1. Part of a plane pattern

altering either the motif or the scheme of repetition (or both, of course). These principles are shown in Figures 2 and 3.

In Figure 2, small parts of four plane patterns are shown. Each pattern has exactly the same scheme of repetition as the pattern in Figure 1 but with a different motif in each case. It should be evident that many more patterns could be constructed using this same scheme and that the total number of these patterns is the same as the total number of different motifs that is available. This number is very large and may even be infinite.

Alternatively the pattern in Figure 1 can be changed by changing the scheme as indicated in Figure 3. Here the

motif is used with two other schemes of repetition to make two different patterns.

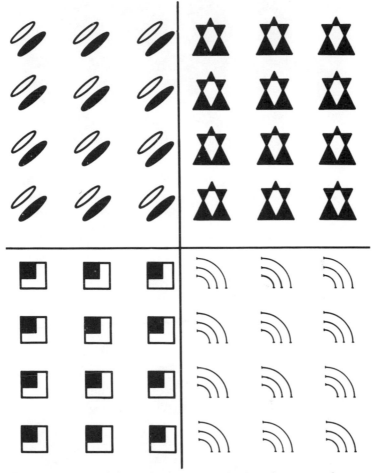

Figure 2. Parts of four plane patterns having the same scheme of repetition as for the pattern in Figure 1

The number of different patterns that can be constructed in this way is the same as the number of different schemes available and this might be thought to be very large. However this is not so! The number is actually very small – five in fact, as will be proven in Chapter 3.

It should now be possible to answer two of the questions posed at the beginning of this chapter: 'what is a pattern?', and 'what are the component parts of a pattern?'. The answers, of course, are that patterns are repetitive assemblies constructed from two separate components, the MOTIF and the SCHEME OF REPETITION. If these answers cannot be appreciated fully then read the first part of the chapter again, for the ideas to be introduced next are based on separate considerations of the scheme of repetition on the one hand and of the motif on the other.

4

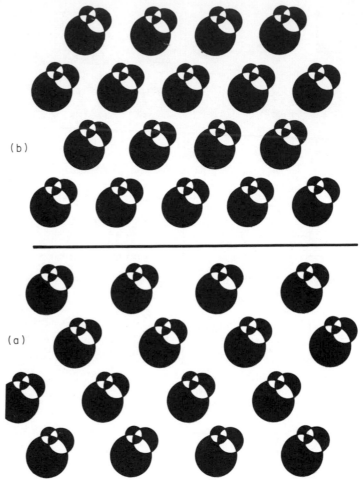

Figure 3. Parts of two plane patterns having the same motif as the pattern in Figure 1 but with different schemes of repetition

CONCEPT No. 1. A PLANE PATTERN CONSISTS OF A MOTIF REPEATED ACCORDING TO A SCHEME OF REPETITION.

The three-dimensional pattern of a crystal is in no way different from a two-dimensional pattern, having both a motif and a scheme of repetition, as shall be seen in Chapter 8. It is frequently necessary to provide a detailed description of the pattern of a crystal so that information about the crystal can be communicated from one person to another, so that the properties of the crystal may be interpreted, so that the crystal may be classified, and for other purposes as well. Consequently, a simple, yet accurate means of describing the pattern is required, and since the pattern comprises two parts it is necessary to describe both the motif and the scheme of repetition. Thus, it is now necessary to proceed with the task of

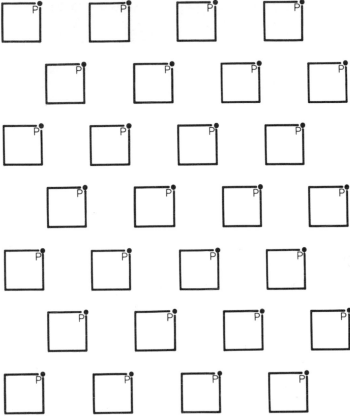

Figure 4. Part of a plane pattern showing an identical point P in each motif

devising the means of making these descriptions for the case of a two-dimensional pattern.

First consider the scheme of repetition. It is required to find some means of specifying precisely the code whereby the unit of the pattern, the motif, is repeated in two dimensions to generate the extended pattern.

To find this code, examine the two-dimensional pattern constructed using the simple square motif shown in Figure 4. In particular, note that a point labelled P has been marked at an identical place in each motif of the pattern. Next, observe that the points alone are arrayed as shown in Figure 5 and specify exactly those places in the pattern where the motifs are located. It is evident, therefore, that the array of points represents the code of the pattern, that is, the scheme of repetition.

CONCEPT No. 2.   THE SCHEME OF REPETITION OF A PATTERN IS
                  SPECIFIED BY AN ARRAY OF POINTS.

It is very important to realize that the same array of points as shown in Figure 5 is obtained from the pattern in Figure 4 regardless of where the representative point

Figure 5. Part of the array of identical points P
obtained from the pattern in Figure 4

for each motif is located, provided only that the point is located at exactly the same place for every motif. This is shown in Figure 6(a), while Figure 6(b) shows that the representative point need not be actually located within the motif at all. The only condition that must be satisfied to obtain the array of points that specifies precisely the scheme of repetition is that each and every point must bear exactly the same relationship with the motif it represents.

CONCEPT No. 3.   EVERY POINT IN THE SCHEME OF REPETITION MUST BEAR EXACTLY THE SAME RELATIONSHIP TO THE MOTIF IT REPRESENTS.

It has now been established that a plane pattern can be separated into a motif and a scheme of repetition, and that the scheme can be specified by an array of points in which each point represents the location of one motif in the pattern.

Conversely, a pattern can be assembled from a scheme of repetition and a particular motif. For example, the motif may be a

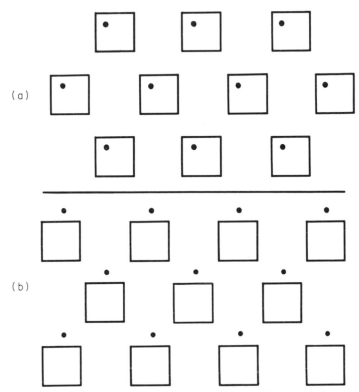

Figure 6. Two parts of the pattern in Figure 4 showing that the same array of points is obtained for any position of the representative point in or near the motif

and the scheme of repetition some particular array of points. This information is sufficient to assemble a pattern. To make the pattern the two parts are simply put together with one triangle motif associated in exactly the same way with each point in the array. Such a pattern is shown in Figure 7. An identical pattern is obtained regardless of where the triangle is located at each point provided only that every triangle is upright and located at the point in the same way. This is absolutely essential to the idea of a pattern as stated in CONCEPT No. 3.

If the requirement stated in CONCEPT No. 3 is not satisfied and the relationship between the motifs and the points of the scheme is not constant, then the combination does not produce a pattern. The absence of a constant relationship between the motifs and the points is demonstrated in Figure 8 which is just an irregular jumble of triangles having no resemblance to a repetitive pattern.

The requirement that each motif and its point be associated in exactly the same way is so rigid that even the slightest misplacement of a single motif would be sufficient to destroy the pattern. However, as will be seen in Chapter 18, it is not always necessary to require that patterns be absolutely perfect if it is admitted that defects in the regularity of the array of motifs may occur. Under these circumstances the slight misplacement of one or more motifs can be regarded as a

Figure 7. Part of the plane pattern obtained by placing a triangle motif in exactly the same way at every one of the points of a scheme of repetition

defect or error that does not invalidate the remainder of the pattern. The idea that defects can occur in patterns becomes very important when considering real crystals for, as will be seen, no matter how carefully a crystal is prepared or handled the pattern of it is always far from perfect. On the other hand, plane patterns, being mostly man-made, are usually quite perfect so that it is now necessary to consider the features of the perfect combination of a motif with a scheme of repetition.

Figure 8. Part of a disorderly array obtained by placing a triangle motif in an arbitrary way at every one of the points of a scheme of repetition

Chapter 2

Plane Lattices

The array of points at which the motifs are located in a perfect pattern is very special and has the property that every point in the array is absolutely indistinguishable from every other point.

What does this mean?

Imagine an ant (a very intelligent ant) to be sitting at one particular point, the point A, in the array shown in Figure 9. Now imagine the ant to examine the surroundings of the point very carefully, taking note of the directions and distances to the nearest points, the next nearest points, and so on. Now imagine the ant to leave point A and proceed on a haphazard walk from point to point in the array. During this walk the ant, despite its intelligence and the measurements it made, can never know whether any of the points it visits is that original point A. The reason for this is that there is nothing to distinguish the point A, for the surroundings of every point in the array are exactly the same as the surroundings of that point so carefully noted by the ant. The point A is indistinguishable from every other point in the array; all points in the array are identical.

Any array of points which has the property that all the points in it are identical must be limitless. There can be no boundary to the array for, as shown in Figure 10, the surroundings of a point such as B on a boundary differ considerably from the surroundings of a point such as C remote from a boundary, and the points B and C would be distinguishable from one another. Thus, an array of indistinguishable points must extend to infinity. It automatically follows that *perfect* patterns (consisting of an identical motif at every point) do not have boundaries and are necessarily infinite in the two dimensions of the plane of the paper or other material on which they occur. As a consequence, it will be appreciated that only a small part of any two-dimensional pattern can be shown in the diagrams in this book or elsewhere. Further, the principle that perfect patterns extend to infinity is true for both two-dimensional and three-dimensional cases, as will be demonstrated in Chapter 18.

CONCEPT No. 4. PERFECT PATTERNS AND THE ASSOCIATED ARRAY OF POINTS SHOWING THE SCHEME OF REPETITION EXTEND TO INFINITY.

It is implicit that the arrangement of points in the infinite array must be absolutely perfect. Any defect or error in the order or regularity of the array would

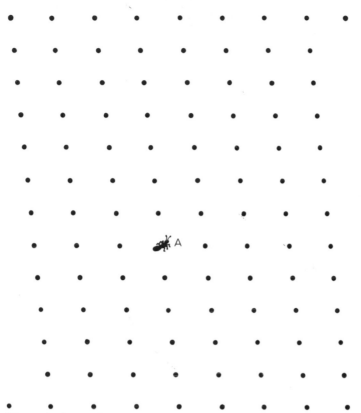

Figure 9. Part of a repetitive array of points with an ant at point A

mean that points at or near the defect would be distinguishable from points remote from the defect. While it may be acceptable that a few errors in the placement of the motifs might occur, it is absolutely unacceptable that any errors in the actual distribution of points can occur; the array is necessarily perfect. This idea is easily accepted if it is remembered that the array has no real physical existence but is merely a mathematical device used to simplify the task of providing a description of a pattern. The perfection of the array ensures that all points in it are identical.

CONCEPT No. 5.   THE POINTS IN THE ARRAY SHOWING THE SCHEME OF REPETITION OF A PATTERN ARE INDISTINGUISH-ABLE FROM ONE ANOTHER.

An array of points all having identical surroundings, indistinguishable from one another, and therefore being perfectly ordered and extending to infinity, is known as a LATTICE. For the two-dimensional case at present being considered, the lattice is termed a PLANE LATTICE. It must be realized that, for the points in a plane lattice to be indistinguishable from one another, not only must the

12

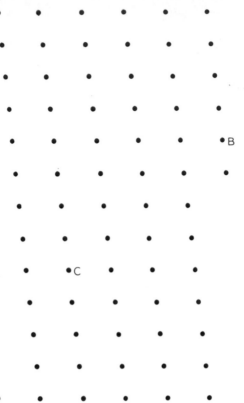

Figure 10. Part of a finite array of points showing that boundary points such as B and interior points such as C have different surroundings

surroundings of each point be identical but the orientation of the surroundings must be identical also. This requirement is demonstrated in Figure 11 which shows in (a) two distinguishable points A and B having the same surroundings but in different orientations, and in (b) two indistinguishable points C and D with the same surroundings in identical orientations.

DEFINITION No. 1.   A PLANE LATTICE IS AN INFINITE ARRAY OF POINTS IN TWO DIMENSIONS SUCH THAT EVERY POINT IS IDENTICAL, HAVING THE SAME SURROUNDINGS IN THE SAME ORIENTATION.

The points which comprise a lattice, whether two or three dimensional, are known as LATTICE POINTS.

DEFINITION No. 2.   A LATTICE POINT IS ANY POINT OF A LATTICE.

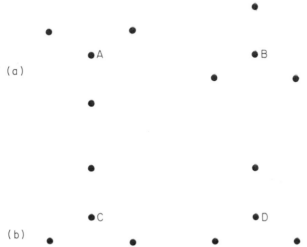

Figure 11. Arrays of points showing (a) points A and B with identical surroundings in different orientations, and (b) points C and D with identical surroundings in the same orientation

Thus, the plane lattice of any two-dimensional pattern is the array of points showing the scheme of repetition for that pattern.

CONCEPT No. 6.   THE PLANE LATTICE OF A TWO-DIMENSIONAL PATTERN IS THAT ARRAY OF POINTS WHICH SPECIFIES THE SCHEME OF REPETITION OF THE PATTERN.

Having now introduced the idea of a lattice as a rather special array of points it is evident that a two-dimensional pattern is properly described in terms of the plane lattice and the motif. Similarly all other patterns are properly described in terms of the appropriate lattice and motif. The problem which needs to be solved next is to discover how to specify a plane lattice with both precision and economy so that the distribution of points in it may be readily communicated. As will now be shown, it is not necessary to draw a portion of the lattice as in Figures 5 and 9 to show the scheme of repetition, for there exists a means of specifying the lattice accurately and with the economy of a simple terminology.

To specify a lattice it is necessary to refer to a very important property of any lattice, the property that the points of it occur in straight lines. Parts of some lines of points are shown for one particular lattice in Figure 12 and a consideration of these lines leads to a number of important conclusions.

First of all it is clear that the lines of points occur in sets and, because the lattice is infinite, each set contains an infinite number of lines and each line is infinitely long.

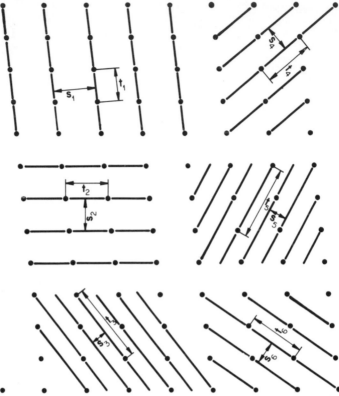

Figure 12. Part of a plane lattice showing small portions of a few of the sets of lines of points that exist in it; each set has a characteristic separation s, and unit translation t

CONCEPT No. 7.   THE POINTS OF A LATTICE OCCUR IN SETS OF STRAIGHT LINES.

In any set, all lines are parallel and the spacing between adjacent lines is identical. Additionally, the distance between points along each line of a set is exactly the same. For convenience, let the perpendicular spacing between adjacent lines be s (the 'line-spacing'), and the separation of the points in any line be t, as shown in Figure 12. The distance t between two adjacent points in any line of any set of lines is called a UNIT TRANSLATION.

DEFINITION No. 3.   A UNIT TRANSLATION IS THE DISTANCE BETWEEN ADJACENT POINTS ALONG ANY LINE IN A LATTICE.

Now the product of s and t, (s x t), is the total area associated with each lattice point and the inverse, $1/(s \times t)$, is the number N of points in each unit area of the lattice (points per square metre). Since this number is a fundamental property of the lattice, it must be independent of the way in which the lines occur through the lattice and therefore the product s x t must have exactly the same value for every set of lines. Careful measurement of the values of s and of t for each of the six sets of lines shown in Figure 12, followed by some simple arithmetic, will show that the product s x t is, in fact, a constant.

The constancy of s x t necessarily means that those sets of lines which have large values of s (widely spaced lines) are the most densely populated with points (points closest together), while closely spaced lines have a large separation between adjacent points, as is clearly shown in Figure 12.

CONCEPT No. 8. THE SETS OF LINES OF POINTS IN A LATTICE ARE CHARACTERIZED BY A SPACING, s, AND A POINT SEPARATION, t, THE PRODUCT OF WHICH, (s x t), IS A CONSTANT FOR THE LATTICE, AND 1/(s x t) IS THE NUMBER, N, OF LATTICE POINTS PER UNIT AREA.

Although only six sets of lines of points are shown in Figure 12, it is easy to see that there are many other sets as well. Since the lattice is infinite, the number of

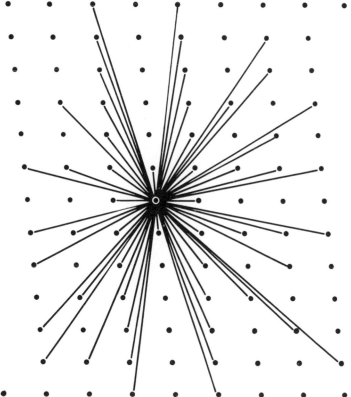

Figure 13. Part of a plane lattice showing a few of the unit translations

sets of lines within it must be infinite. Each of these sets has a characteristic value for s and for t and, of course, the product s × t is the same for every one of the infinite number of sets.

CONCEPT No. 9.   AN INFINITE NUMBER OF DIFFERENT SETS OF LINES OCCUR THROUGH THE POINTS OF ANY LATTICE.

Since there is an infinite number of sets of lines each with a characteristic unit translation t there must be an infinite number of different unit translations for any lattice. These unit translations are best visualized as the lines joining any particular lattice point to the nearest point in every possible direction. Some unit translations of a lattice are shown in Figure 13.

CONCEPT No. 10.   THERE IS AN INFINITE NUMBER OF UNIT TRANS-LATIONS IN EVERY LATTICE

It will now be demonstrated that these unit translations can be used to provide the means of describing accurately the plane lattice of any plane pattern.

Chapter 3

The Unit Cell of a Plane Lattice

Any two sets of non-parallel lines, selected from the infinite number of sets through the points of a plane lattice, divide the plane of the lattice into small sections as shown in Figure 14. Each small section is a quadrilateral, specifically a parallelogram. The edges of the parallelogram are the unit translations for the two selected sets of lines, and the corners of the parallelograms are located at the points of the lattice.

Note that Figure 14 shows only a few of the parallelograms obtained from the two sets of selected lines. Since the lattice is infinite and all lines in it are infinitely long, there must be an infinite number of these parallelograms. Every parallelogram has exactly the same shape and size since the edges are the unit translations of the two sets of lines and the corners are the points of the lattice. As every parallelogram is identical, any single one of them must be representative of the rest. If the dimensions which specify the size and shape of one single parallelogram are known, then all other parallelograms are also specified and, if all parallelograms are specified, the lattice of points on which the parallelograms are based must be specified too.

The known dimensions of one parallelogram enables it to be constructed on a sheet of paper or other material, and then to be repeated over and over to completely cover the plane (as in Figure 14). The plane lattice is then obtained simply by placing points at the corners of all the parallelograms. Thus it is seen that the plane lattice is completely specified by the dimensions of one parallelogram.

This parallelogram, which is so perfectly representative that it can be used to construct the lattice, is known as a UNIT CELL.

DEFINITION No. 4. A UNIT CELL OF A PLANE LATTICE IS A
PARALLELOGRAM OF TWO UNIT TRANSLATIONS
WITH LATTICE POINTS AT THE CORNERS AND IS
PERFECTLY REPRESENTATIVE OF THE LATTICE.

The assembly of unit cells shown in Figure 14 is only one way in which the subdivision of the plane of a lattice into small representative parts can be accomplished. Other pairs of sets of lines achieve a similar result — dividing the plane into identical parallelograms or unit cells, each having the unit translations of the lines as edges and lattice points at the corners. Figure 15 shows the unit cells obtained from seven different combinations of two unit translations.

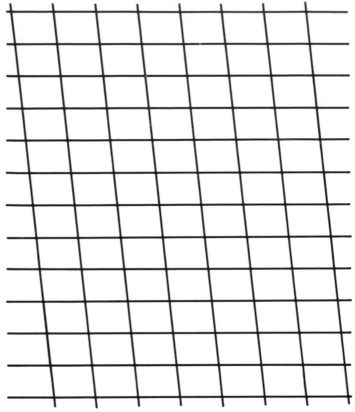

Figure 14. Diagram showing that any two sets of lines in a plane lattice divides the plane into identical parallelograms

Since there is an infinite number of different sets of lines through the points of a plane lattice, there must be an infinite number of combinations of two different sets and so an infinite number of different unit cells. Each of these unit cells is perfectly representative of the lattice and could equally well be used to construct it if the appropriate dimensions are known.

CONCEPT No. 11.   THERE IS AN INFINITE NUMBER OF DIFFERENT UNIT CELLS WHICH CAN BE USED TO DESCRIBE ANY LATTICE.

The dimensions of any unit cell are simply those parameters which must be assigned values to specify the shape and the size of that cell. Since the unit cell is a parallelogram it is completely specified by the lengths a and b of the two sides, and the angle α between them, as shown in Figure 16.

The lengths a and b are the distances between lattice points along the two sets of lines which produced the unit cell and so are the unit translations for those lines.

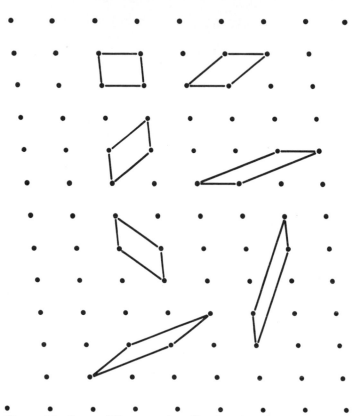

Figure 15. Seven different unit cells of a plane lattice obtained from seven different combinations of two unit translations

CONCEPT No. 12.   THE UNIT CELL IS COMPLETELY SPECIFIED BY THE LENGTHS OF THE TWO EDGES (THE UNIT TRANSLATIONS), AND THE ANGLE BETWEEN THEM.

The unit translations and included angle specifying the size and shape of a unit cell are termed the LATTICE PARAMETERS of the cell.

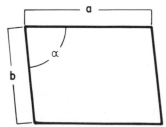

Figure 16. Diagram showing that the size and shape of the parallelogram unit cell is specified by the parameters a, b and α

DEFINITION No. 5. THE LATTICE PARAMETERS OF A UNIT CELL ARE
THOSE UNIT TRANSLATIONS AND ANGLES WHICH
MUST BE ASSIGNED VALUES TO SPECIFY THE
DIMENSIONS OF THE CELL.

There are three important questions concerning unit cells that must now be answered.

The first relates to the number of different patterns that can be constructed using the same motif. This problem arose in Chapter 1 and, as was mentioned there, the number of such patterns is the same as the number of different schemes of repetition, that is, the number of different plane lattices. Since every plane lattice can be represented by a unit cell, the number of different plane lattices must be the same as the number of 'basically different' unit cells. Consequently, it is now necessary to discover the number of different ways in which it is possible to construct a parallelogram unit cell. The answer is five – a surprisingly small number.

The five 'basically different' parallelograms shown in Figure 17 indicate that the

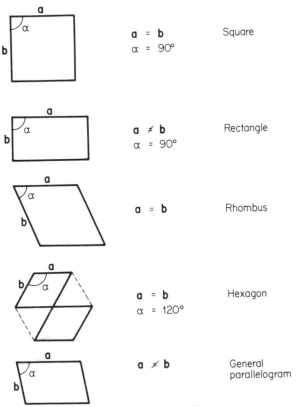

Figure 17. The five different kinds of parallelogram

five different plane lattices are based on the square, the rectangle, the rhombus, the hexagon, and the general parallelogram unit cells.

CONCEPT No. 13.   THERE ARE FIVE DIFFERENT PLANE LATTICES.

An array of unit cells in the plane of any lattice (such as shown in Figure 14) necessarily subdivides the plane pattern, from which the lattice was derived, into those unit cells.

Referring back to Chapter 1, it will be seen that the patterns shown in Figures 1 and 2 can be represented by a rectangle unit cell, the pattern shown in Figure 3(a) can be represented by a hexagon unit cell, and the patterns shown in Figures 3(b), 4, and 7 can be represented by general parallelogram unit cells.

It might be argued that an infinite number of different patterns, all with the same motif, could be constructed on the square lattice for example, since $a = b$ can have an infinite number of different values. While it is true that $a = b$ can have an infinity of values, all patterns derived from a square cell are 'basically the same' for it is not the particular lengths of a and b that are important, only the equality of them. Similarly all rectangle unit cells are basically the same regardless of the actual lengths of a and b provided only that $a \neq b$ and that $\alpha = 90°$, all rhombuses are basically the same regardless of the values of $a = b$ and of α, all hexagons are basically the same regardless of the value of $a = b$ provided only that $\alpha = 120°$, and all general parallelograms are basically the same regardless of the values of a, b, and α.

The meaning of 'basically the same' is best explained in terms of the symmetry properties of the lattice examined in Chapter 4.

The second question concerns the number of lattice points associated with each unit cell.

How many lattice points does a unit cell contain? This is an important property of the lattice for, as there is one motif at each lattice point, the number of points in each unit cell is the same as the number of motifs in each unit cell of the pattern.

Initially it might appear that each cell contains four points, one at each corner, but this is quite incorrect, as is shown in Figure 18. In this diagram the lattice

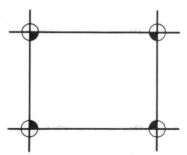

Figure 18. Diagram showing that only part of the lattice point at each corner of a unit cell is associated with that cell

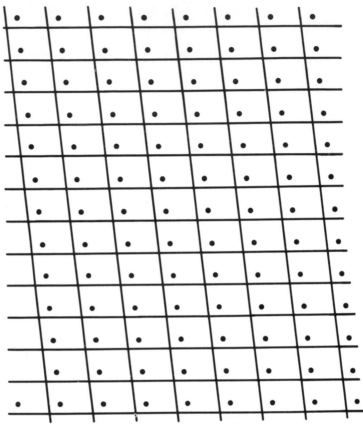

Figure 19. Diagram showing that a small displacement of the
assembly of unit cells relative to the array of lattice points leaves
a single point in each cell

points have been grossly enlarged to demonstrate that each one of them is shared
by the neighbouring cells. Only part of each point is associated with any particular
cell. As should be obvious, each point is shared by four cells so that, regardless of
the type of unit cell, on average one-quarter of each point is within each of those
four cells. Since there are four shared points for each cell, the total number of
points in any one cell is 4 x 0.25 = 1. Each cell contains exactly one lattice point.
This can be demonstrated easily and more vividly by slightly displacing the array of
unit cells (shown in Figure 14) relative to the plane lattice, as is shown in Figure 19.
Clearly one point and one point only is associated with each cell of the lattice.

The special term that is used to designate a unit cell which contains only one
lattice point is PRIMITIVE UNIT CELL or SIMPLE UNIT CELL. Note that all the
unit cells shown in Figure 15 are primitive unit cells.

DEFINITION No. 6.   A PRIMITIVE UNIT CELL CONTAINS A SINGLE
LATTICE POINT.

It follows that if a primitive unit cell contains one lattice point then any unit cell containing more than one lattice point necessarily must be non-primitive.

DEFINITION No. 7.   A NON-PRIMITIVE UNIT CELL CONTAINS TWO OR MORE LATTICE POINTS.

Figure 20 shows part of the same lattice as in Figure 15 but with a few of the infinite number of possible non-primitive unit cells obtained by appropriate combinations of two unit translations. Examine these unit cells closely to see first of all that each of them is representative of the lattice and by repetition would reproduce it exactly. Therefore they are true unit cells with size and shape determined by the three lattice parameters a, b, and α. However, also note that each cell contains, in addition to the points at the corners, lattice points wholly within the cell. These cells are non-primitive by DEFINITION No. 7 and all happen to be general parallelograms.

It is instructive to determine how many points each cell contains. Cell (a) has a point at each corner shared with four other cells and which consequently

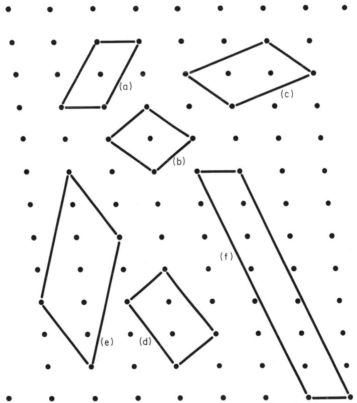

Figure 20. Six different non-primitive unit cells of the same plane lattice as shown in Figure 15

contribute 4 x 0.25 = 1 point, which together with the point at the centre make a total of two lattice points in the cell. Thus, the cell (a) contains two lattice points. Likewise cell (b) contains two lattice points, cell (c) contains three, cell (d) contains three, cell (e) contains six, and cell (f) contains seven points. There is really no limit to the number of points that a cell may contain but of course, as the number increases so the cell becomes more and more complex and it becomes more and more difficult to specify exactly where the points are located in the cell.

As was established in CONCEPT No. 12, the size and shape of any unit cell is completely specified by the two unit translations and the angle between them, that is by the lattice parameters. No further information is needed to obtain the lattice from a primitive unit cell since the lattice points are located only at the cell corners. However, for non-primitive cells additional parameters must be given to locate the lattice points within the cell and so the specification of a non-primitive unit cell is usually more complicated than the specification of a primitive unit cell. The manner in which the positions of points within a cell can be specified will be examined in Chapter 5.

Referring back now to examine the sizes of the unit cells shown in Figures 14, 15, and 20 brings forth another important property of plane lattices. This is the property that the areas of all possible unit cells are very simply related to one another.

Each of the cells shown in Figure 14 is primitive, as each contains a single lattice point. Each unit cell is identical with all the others and the cells completely cover the plane. Therefore, the area of each unit cell is the same as the total area of the plane divided by the total number of cells or, equivalently, the total number of lattice points on the plane. Thus the area A of a primitive unit cell is the area associated with each lattice point which, as indicated in CONCEPT No. 8 is the inverse of the number N of lattice points per unit area. Clearly $A = 1/N = s \times t$, where s is the spacing and t is the unit translation for any set of lines in the lattice. It is important to realize that the constant $s \times t$ discussed in Chapter 2 has now been identified as the area A of a primitive unit cell of the lattice.

Now refer to Figure 15 which shows seven different unit cells for the same lattice. Since these cells are all primitive, the area of each is the area associated with one lattice point. Thus the area of each of the seven primitive cells shown is exactly the same as the area of the infinity of other primitive unit cells which could be used equally well to represent the lattice.

CONCEPT No. 14.   FOR ANY PARTICULAR PLANE LATTICE, THE INFINITE NUMBER OF DIFFERENT PRIMITIVE UNIT CELLS WHICH CAN BE USED TO REPRESENT IT ALL HAVE EXACTLY THE SAME AREA, THE AREA A PER LATTICE POINT.

Since no unit cell can contain less than a single lattice point, it follows that a primitive cell of any lattice is the smallest cell that can be used to represent that lattice.

The non-primitive unit cells shown in Figure 20 contain small integral (whole) numbers of lattice points. The cell (a) contains two lattice points so the area must be the area associated with two lattice points and which is exactly twice the area of a primitive unit cell. Similarly, the cell (c), containing three lattice points, has an area exactly three-times that of a primitive unit cell, and so on.

CONCEPT No. 15.   THE AREA OF ANY UNIT CELL IN A PLANE LATTICE IS THE PRODUCT OF n AND A, WHERE n IS THE NUMBER OF LATTICE POINTS IN THE UNIT CELL AND A IS THE AREA OF A PRIMITIVE UNIT CELL OF THAT LATTICE.

For example, if the area of a primitive unit cell is 60 square millimetres (mm^2), then a unit cell containing two lattice points has an area of $120\ mm^2$, a unit cell containing four lattice points has an area of $240\ mm^2$ etc.

Notwithstanding the relationship between the area of a unit cell and the number of lattice points it contains, the actual area of any unit cell is determined by the lattice parameters and is given by

$$\text{area} = \mathbf{ab} \sin \alpha,$$

where $\mathbf{a}$, $\mathbf{b}$, and α are the lattice parameters.

The third question now arises. Of the infinity of primitive and non-primitive unit cells available to represent a particular plane lattice, which is the one usually chosen, and why is that particular cell chosen in preference to all others? It has been established that any cell represents the lattice perfectly but the one generally selected is that particular cell that has the simplest geometry. Why choose a complicated cell when a simple one is available? However what does this really mean?

Referring back, Figure 17 indicates that to specify the five different unit cells it is necessary to assign values to one, two, or three lattice parameters as follows.

KIND OF CELL		PARAMETERS WHICH MUST BE ASSIGNED VALUES TO SPECIFY THE SIZE AND SHAPE OF THE CELL
SQUARE	$\mathbf{a} = \mathbf{b}; \alpha = 90°$	$\mathbf{a}$
HEXAGON	$\mathbf{a} = \mathbf{b}; \alpha = 120°$	$\mathbf{a}$
RECTANGLE	$\mathbf{a} \neq \mathbf{b}; \alpha = 90°$	$\mathbf{a}, \mathbf{b}$
RHOMBUS	$\mathbf{a} = \mathbf{b}; \alpha \neq 90°$	$\mathbf{a}, \alpha$
GENERAL PARALLELOGRAM	$\mathbf{a} \neq \mathbf{b}; \alpha \neq 90°$	$\mathbf{a}, \mathbf{b}, \alpha$

In this list the simplest cell is at the top and the most complex at the bottom. Consequently, if it is at all possible, a cell high on the list is always preferred to one lower on the list for representation of a particular lattice. The lower the cell on the list the greater is the number of parameters needed to specify it and the more difficult it is to construct.

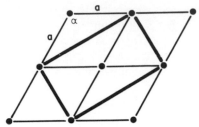

Figure 21. Diagram showing that the rhombus unit cell (light lines) is equivalent to a rectangle unit cell (heavy lines) with a lattice point at the geometrical centre

CONCEPT No. 16.   THE UNIT CELL WHICH IS USUALLY USED TO REPRESENT A PLANE LATTICE IS THAT CELL WHICH IS GEOMETRICALLY THE SIMPLEST.

It should be evident that non-primitive unit cells, such as those shown in Figure 20, are more complicated than primitive unit cells such as those shown in Figure 15, since additional parameters may be needed to specify the locations o points within the cells. The only non-primitive unit cells for which additiona parameters are not necessary are those such as shown in Figure 20(a), (b). These cells contain just one additional point, which, being located at the geometrica centre of the cell, needs no parameters to specify the position. Such a cell is said to be CENTRED.

CONCEPT No. 17.   A CENTRED UNIT CELL HAS LATTICE POINTS AT THE CORNERS TOGETHER WITH AN ADDITIONAL POINT AT THE GEOMETRICAL CENTRE.

It is worth noting that in some classifications of plane lattices the rhombus unit cell is omitted, for, as shown in Figure 21, the plane lattice represented by a rhombus unit cell (light lines) can equally well be represented by a rectangle unit cell (heavy lines), with lattice points at the corners and at the centre. This unit cell is termed a centred rectangle unit cell and is certainly easier to specify and to construct than the equivalent primitive rhombus unit cell.

Chapter 4

Simple Symmetry

In discussing the unit cells of the five different kinds of plane lattice it was stressed that the greater the number of parameters needed to specify a cell the more complex is that cell. This complexity is determined in fact by the SYMMETRY PROPERTIES of the arrays of points in the five lattices. Also, a little earlier, in Chapter 3 it was pointed out that all square unit cells are 'basically the same', all rectangle unit cells are 'basically the same', and so on, and that the term 'basically the same' referred to the SYMMETRY of the lattice. It is now appropriate to consider the property of SYMMETRY to see what it means.

Examine the square ABCD shown in perspective in Figure 22 and imagine it to be rotated about the line xy passing at right angles through the centre p. Clearly, after a rotation of 90° from the starting position shown, the corner A will be moved to the position originally occupied by the corner B, B will be moved to the position originally occupied by the corner C, and so on. The new position of the square is obviously not distinguishable from the position before the rotation. The initial and final positions are completely indistinguishable from one another and for this reason the rotation of 90° about the line xy is said to move or transform the square to SELF COINCIDENCE.

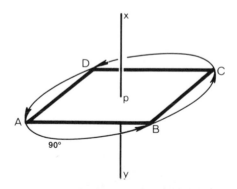

Figure 22. Diagram showing that the square ABCD can be transformed to self coincidence by rotation through 90°, 180°, 270°, and 360° about the line xy passing at right angles through the centre p

CONCEPT No. 18.   TWO OR MORE POSITIONS OF A BODY THAT ARE
INDISTINGUISHABLE FROM ONE ANOTHER ARE SELF
COINCIDENT POSITIONS.

For rotation of the square through an additional $90°$, that is $180°$ in all, the corner A will be in the position originally occupied by C, B will be in the position originally occupied by D, etc., so that this rotation also transforms the square to self coincidence. It should be clear that each additional $90°$ of rotation will transform the square to self coincidence.

An operation such as the rotation just considered which transforms a body – any body – to self coincidence is termed a SYMMETRY OPERATION and the body is said to have symmetry with respect to that operation.

DEFINITION No. 8.   A SYMMETRY OPERATION IS ANY OPERATION THAT
CAN BE PERFORMED ON A BODY TO TRANSFORM IT
TO SELF COINCIDENCE.

Now examine the rotation operation performed on the square ABCD in a little more detail. It has been established that self coincidence occurs at every $90°$ of rotation, so that during a rotation of $360°$ through a full circle self coincidence will occur four-times (i.e. $360°/90° = 4$). For this reason the square is said to have 4-fold rotational symmetry about the line xy. Consequently the line xy is a rather special line, for rotation about it transforms the square to these particular positions of self coincidence and the line is termed a ROTATION AXIS OF SYMMETRY.

DEFINITION No. 9.   A ROTATION AXIS OF SYMMETRY IS ANY LINE
ABOUT WHICH A BODY MAY BE ROTATED TO ONE OR
MORE POSITIONS OF SELF COINCIDENCE.

The term AXIS simply refers to any line which has some special property or use

DEFINITION No. 10. AN AXIS IS ANY LINE IN A PATTERN OR LATTICE
THAT SERVES A USEFUL PURPOSE IN SPECIFYING
THE PROPERTIES OF THAT PATTERN OR LATTICE.

It has now been seen that one kind of symmetry operation is rotation through some critical angle about a special line. This line, the rotation axis is termed SYMMETRY ELEMENT. After examination of the other kinds of symmetry element the term will be defined precisely in DEFINITION No. 14.

The quality of a rotation axis is measured by the number of times during a full $360°$ rotation that the body is transformed to self coincident positions. If that number is N then the axis is termed an N-fold rotation axis and the rotation angle between successive positions of self coincidence is $360°/N$. The higher the value of N, the higher is the rotational symmetry of the body. Equivalently, since θ is the angle between the successive positions, then the rotation axis is a $360°/\theta = N$-fold axis.

DEFINITION No. 11. AN N-FOLD ROTATION AXIS OF SYMMETRY IS A LINE ABOUT WHICH A BODY IS TRANSFORMED TO SELF COINCIDENCE N TIMES DURING A 360° ROTATION. THE ANGLE θ BETWEEN THE SELF COINCIDENT POSITIONS IS 360°/N.

There are a number of different kinds of rotation axis depending on the shape of the body with the rotational symmetry. As shown in Figure 23(a), rotation through 180° about the line which passes at right angles through the centre of the rectangle transforms it to self coincidence and so the line is a 360°/180° = 2-fold axis. This kind of rotation axis is identified by the symbol ⬬. Similarly the line through the centre of the parallelogram in Figure 23(b) is a ⬬ axis. It should be easy to see that the lines through the centres of the polygons in Figure 23 are rotation axes as follows.

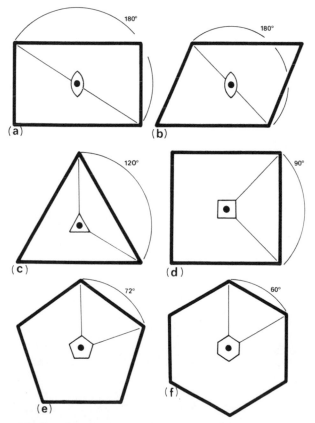

Figure 23. Polygons having 2-fold, 3-fold, 4-fold, 5-fold, and 6-fold rotation axes

30

(a) $\theta = 180°$ $N = 360°/180° = 2$;   2-fold axis; symbol

(b) $\theta = 180°$ $N = 3\text{L}0°/180° = 2$;   2-fold axis; symbol

(c) $\theta = 120°$ $N = 360°/120° = 3$;   3-fold axis; symbol

(d) $\theta = 90°$ $N = 360°/90° = 4$;   4-fold axis; symbol

(e) $\theta = 72°$ $N = 360°/72° = 5$;   5-fold axis; symbol

(f) $\theta = 60°$ $N = 360°/60° = 6$;   6-fold axis; symbol

Clearly, the quality of the rotational symmetry of the polygons increases from (a) and (b) through (c), (d), and (e) to (f). Equally clearly, any axis which does not pass through the geometrical centre of a polygon must be a 1-fold rotation axis for it is necessary to rotate the polygon through a full 360° about such an axis to

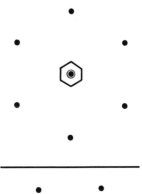

Figure 24. A hexagonal plane lattice showing the location of 3-fold and 6-fold rotation axes

transform it to self coincidence. Thus, most arbitrary axes are 1-fold axes and it is only that special line through the geometrical centre of a regular polygon that has higher order symmetry, i.e. is at least a 2-fold axis.

So far, these considerations of rotational symmetry have been quite general, being applied to various regular polygons. It is now necessary to extend the application to the unit cells of the five plane lattices. Can all the rotation axes shown in Figure 23 occur in these plane lattices? Are there any other rotation axes that can occur? The answer to both questions is no. Only the 2-fold, 3-fold, 4-fold, and 6-fold axes (together with the trivial 1-fold axes) can occur, as it is not possible for any plane lattice to contain a 5-fold axis. The basis for this limitation is simply that the unit cell of a plane lattice is a parallelogram (DEFINITION No. 4), which when repeated over and over will completely cover a plane. The 2-fold axes shown in Figure 23(a), (b) occur in the rectangle and general parallelogram unit cells respectively (see Figure 17), while the 4-fold axis shown in Figure 23(d) occurs in the square unit cell. The 3-fold and 6-fold axes shown in Figure 23(c), (f) are related to the hexagon unit cell, as is shown in Figure 24.

The pentagon shown in Figure 23(e) is not contained within any of the five different plane lattices and so 5-fold rotational symmetry cannot occur in these lattices. For the same reason 7-fold, 8-fold, and the higher order rotation axes cannot exist as it is impossible for rotation about such axes to transform a lattice represented by a parallelogram unit cell to self coincidence.

CONCEPT No. 19. PLANE LATTICES HAVE AT LEAST 2-FOLD, 3-FOLD, 4-FOLD, OR 6-FOLD ROTATION AXES OF SYMMETRY.

It is now necessary to extend the idea of rotational symmetry from the plane lattice to the plane pattern. Examine Figure 25(a), (b), (c), showing parts of patterns for which the unit cell is a square and so would be expected to have a 4-fold rotation axis through the centre (see Figure 23(d)). In Figure 25(a), the motif is a square centred at each lattice point and rotation about the line passing through the centre of the unit cell clearly transforms the pattern to self coincidence after every $90°$ of rotation. Thus the rotation axis is a $360°/90° = 4$-fold axis, and the rotational symmetry of the pattern is the same as the rotational symmetry of the lattice. This comes about because the symmetry of the (square) motif is the same as the symmetry of the (square) lattice. If the symmetry of the motif is lower than that of the lattice then necessarily the symmetry of the pattern is lower than that of the lattice, as shown in Figure 25(b), (c). In (b) the motif is a rectangle centred on the lattice points so that, for this pattern, rotation about the line through the centre of the square unit cell transforms it to self coincidence not after $90°$ but after $180°$. Consequently, because of the shape of the motif, the rotation axis is only a $360°/180° = 2$-fold axis as indicated.

Similarly, as shown in (c), rotation about the line through the centre of the square unit cell transforms the pattern with a triangle motif to self coincidence only after $360°$ and so, for this pattern, the line is a $360°/360° = 1$-fold axis.

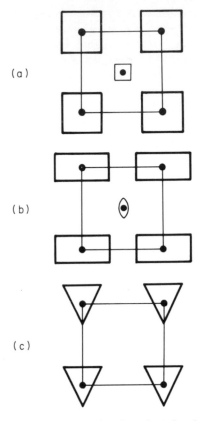

Figure 25. Diagrams showing that the shape of the motif located at the points of a square lattice influences the kind of rotation axis that passes through the centre of the unit cell

CONCEPT No. 20.   THE ROTATIONAL SYMMETRY OF A PLANE PATTERN DEPENDS NOT ONLY IN THE ROTATIONAL SYMMETRY OF THE LATTICE BUT ALSO ON THE SHAPE OF THE MOTIF.

This concept is also demonstrated in Figure 26 in which the 6-fold axis associated with the hexagonal lattice remains a 6-fold axis in (a), but becomes a 3-fold axis in (b), and a 1-fold axis in (c) because of the shape of the motif.

It will be noted that, while all plane lattices have at least 2-fold rotational symmetry, a plane pattern, constructed from a motif having either no rotational symmetry as in Figure 26(c), or rotational symmetry quite different from that of the lattice as in Figure 25(c), may have no rotational symmetry at all, i.e. only 1-fold rotation axes.

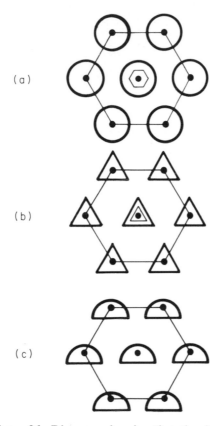

(a)

(b)

(c)

Figure 26. Diagrams showing that the shape of the motif located at the points of a hexagonal lattice influences the kind of rotation axis that it contains

CONCEPT No. 21.   PLANE PATTERNS CONTAIN 1-FOLD, 2-FOLD, 3-FOLD, 4-FOLD OR 6-FOLD AXES OF ROTATIONAL SYMMETRY.

These symmetry elements are signified by the following numerical symbols.

1-fold axis: 1
2-fold axis: 2
3-fold axis: 3
4-fold axis: 4
6-fold axis: 6

It should be evident also that, while the shape of the motif may lower the rotational symmetry of a pattern compared with the symmetry of the lattice, in no way can the symmetry be increased by the shape of the motif. This is demonstrated

34

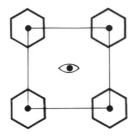

Figure 27. Diagram showing that a hexagon motif located at the points of a square lattice produces only a 2-fold rotation axis through the centre of the unit cell

in Figure 27 in which the 4-fold rotation axis of a square lattice is reduced to a 2-fold axis by a highly symmetrical hexagonal motif.

CONCEPT No. 22.   THE HIGHEST ROTATIONAL SYMMETRY WHICH OCCURS IN A PLANE PATTERN IS THE ROTATIONAL SYMMETRY OF THE PLANE LATTICE.

It is important to realize that a plane lattice or a plane pattern may contain various rotation axes, as shown in Figure 28. In (a) the positions of 2-fold and 4-fold axes are shown for a square pattern, and in (b) the positions of 2-fold, 3-fold, and 6-fold axes are shown for a hexagonal pattern.

Combinations such as 2-fold and 4-fold, 2-fold and 6-fold, 3-fold and 6-fold, obviously can occur in the same pattern, as is shown in Figure 28, but there are other combinations that cannot possibly occur together. Examples are 3-fold and 4-fold axes, 4-fold and 6-fold axes.

So far the examination of symmetry has been concerned only with rotation, but a symmetry operation is, by DEFINITION No. 8, any operation which can be performed on a body to transform it to self coincidence. There are operations other than rotation that can also achieve self coincidence when applied to a body.

Consider the square ABCD which, as shown in perspective in Figure 29(a), is intersected along the diagonal AC by the plane m. Now, for the condition that the plane m is perpendicular to the square ABCD, reflection across it will interchange the corners D and B, and the initial and final positions of the square are self coincident. Thus mirror reflection by the plane m is a symmetry operation and the plane is a symmetry element called a MIRROR PLANE designated m. There are four planes, shown in Figure 29(b) which reflect a square to self coincidence, and it is important to note from Figure 29(c) that these planes intersect along the 4-fold rotation axis.

DEFINITION No. 12. A MIRROR PLANE OF SYMMETRY IS ANY PLANE WHICH DIVIDES A BODY INTO HALVES THAT ARE MIRROR IMAGES OF ONE ANOTHER ACROSS THE PLANE.

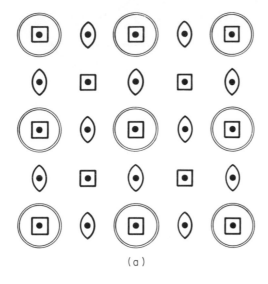

(a)

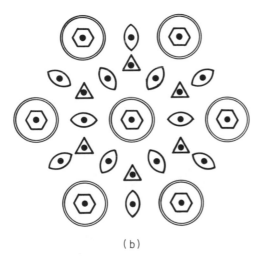

(b)

Figure 28. Diagrams showing: (a) the locations of 2-fold and 4-fold rotation axes perpendicular to a square array of circular motifs; and (b) the locations of 2-fold, 3-fold, and 6-fold rotation axes perpendicular to a hexagonal array of circular motifs

The four mirror planes of a square also occur in a square lattice of course, but whether they occur in a square pattern depends on the shape of the motif as shown in Figure 30. It is evident that the less symmetrical the motif, the fewer are the mirror planes that are present.

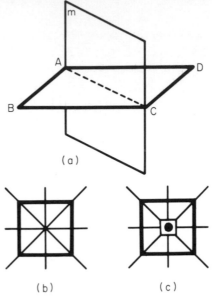

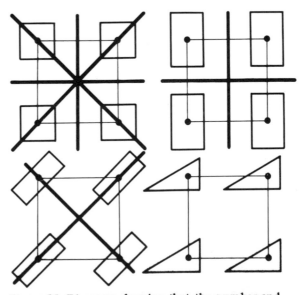

Figure 29. Diagrams showing: (a) a plane m that divides the square ABCD into two mirror-imaged halves; (b) the four mirror planes perpendicular to a square; and (c) the 4-fold rotation axis along the line of intersection of the four mirror planes

Figure 30. Diagrams showing that the number and location of the mirror planes (heavy lines) passing through a square pattern depend on the shape of the motifs located at the points of the lattice

CONCEPT No. 23.　　DEPENDING ON THE SHAPE OF THE MOTIF, THE
　　　　　　　　　　NUMBER OF MIRROR PLANES IN A PLANE PATTERN
　　　　　　　　　　MAY BE LESS THAN THE NUMBER IN THE LATTICE
　　　　　　　　　　OF THE PATTERN.

It is informative to construct unit cells of the five plane lattices and find the locations in them of the mirror planes as follows.

LATTICE　　　　　　　　　NUMBER OF MIRROR PLANES

Square　　　　　　　　　　4 (as shown in Figure 25(b))
Rectangle　　　　　　　　 2
Rhombus　　　　　　　　　 2
General parallelogram　　　 Nil
Hexagon　　　　　　　　　 6 (several unit cells need to be
　　　　　　　　　　　　　　　drawn to find the locations
　　　　　　　　　　　　　　　of the planes (see Figure 17)).

There is one other kind of symmetry operation which can be performed on a planar body to transform it to self coincidence. This operation is demonstrated in Figure 31 which shows an irregular polygon within which is the point p. This point is a special point for it exactly bisects every line drawn through it from one side of the polygon to the other. Thus the two lengths ap and a'p are the same, the lengths bp and b'p are the same, and so on for other lines such as cc' and dd'. It follows that for any point, say e, on the boundary of the polygon the straight line from it through p to an equal distance on the other side produces e' which is also on the boundary. This relationship is true for all points on the boundary as well as within

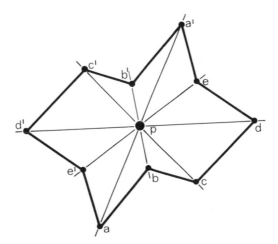

Figure 31.　An irregular polygon with a centre
of symmetry located at the point p

the polygon. The process of using the point p to obtain e′ from e is called INVERSION and the point p is called the CENTRE OF SYMMETRY or simply the CENTRE with numerical symbol $\bar{1}$ (spoken: bar one), and graphical symbol ● .

DEFINITION No. 13. A BODY HAS A CENTRE OF SYMMETRY IF FOR EVERY POINT IN IT THERE IS AN IDENTICAL POINT EQUIDISTANT FROM THE CENTRE BUT ON THE OPPOSITE SIDE.

If every point within a body can be inverted through a centre then the body is transformed to self coincidence by the inversion. Thus the inversion must be a symmetry operation and the centre must be a symmetry element.

CONCEPT No. 24.   A BODY IS INVERTED THROUGH A CENTRE OF SYMMETRY BY PROJECTING EVERY POINT OF IT TO A NEW LOCATION EXACTLY THE SAME DISTANCE FROM THE CENTRE BUT ON THE OPPOSITE SIDE.

Each of the unit cells of the five plane lattices shown in Figure 17 obviously has a centre of symmetry located at the point of intersection of a rotation axis with the plane of the lattice. The rotation axis may be 2-fold, 4-fold, or 6-fold as in Figure 23(a), (b), (d) or (f) and it should be noted that, for two-dimensional figures, patterns or lattices, the symmetry operation of inversion is exactly equivalent to the symmetry operation of rotation but this in no way invalidates the concept of inversion or the concept of a centre of symmetry.

CONCEPT No. 25.   UNIT CELLS OF ALL PLANE LATTICES HAVE A CENTRE OF SYMMETRY.

As in the cases of the other symmetry elements, the presence or absence of a centre in a plane pattern depends upon the shape of the motif as shown in Figure 32. In (a) each motif can be inverted through the centre of the cell to transform the pattern, and therefore the cell also, to self coincidence. Thus the centre of the cell must be a centre of symmetry of the pattern. In (b) the motif cannot be inverted to transform the pattern to self coincidence and so the centre of the cell is not a centre of symmetry of the pattern. Figure 32(c) shows that

inversion of the △ motif of (b) through a centre transforms it to ▽ which is not the motif of the pattern, thereby proving that the pattern in (b) does not have a centre of symmetry.

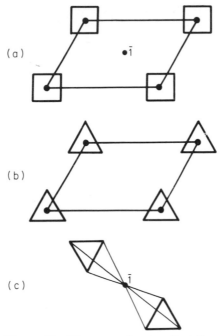

Figure 32. Diagrams showing that the shape of the motif located at the points of a general parallelogram unit cell determine whether or not a centre of symmetry exists

CONCEPT No. 26.   WHETHER A UNIT CELL OF A PLANE PATTERN HAS A CENTRE OF SYMMETRY DEPENDS ON THE SHAPE OF THE MOTIF.

All the symmetry operations which can transform a plane lattice or a plane pattern to self coincidence have now been considered. They are rotation by any of the five elements, 1, 2, 3, 4, 6, mirror reflection by the element m, and inversion by the element $\bar{1}$. Thus there are seven symmetry elements which can occur in plane patterns or lattices. Every lattice or pattern is transformed to self coincidence by the operation of at least one of these elements.

DEFINITION No. 14. A SYMMETRY ELEMENT IS ANY POINT, LINE OR PLANE IN A BODY ABOUT WHICH AN APPROPRIATE SYMMETRY OPERATION WILL TRANSFORM THE BODY TO SELF COINCIDENCE.

The totality of the elements which can operate in a particular lattice or pattern is a qualitative measure of the symmetry. If the number of elements is small the symmetry is low, but if the number is large then the symmetry is high. In one extreme case the only symmetry element which will transform a pattern to self coincidence is a 1-fold rotation axis, as for example in the pattern shown in Figure 32(b). This pattern does not have a centre, has no mirror planes of symmetry, and all the axes through the cell are 1-fold rotation axes. The presence of this sole 1-fold element effectively means that the pattern has no symmetry at all. On the other hand a pattern may contain two or even three kinds of rotation axis, many mirror planes, and a centre. Such a pattern is shown in Figure 25(a) and has high symmetry since it has a large number of symmetry elements.

It is very important to note that the symmetry operations are concerned only with shapes and not with sizes. A square lattice has the same 2-fold and 4-fold rotation axes, the same mirror planes, and the same centre, regardless of whether the distance between lattice points is 10 mm, 100 mm, or 1000 mm. Thus, from the point of view of symmetry, all square lattices are identical and therefore there is only one square lattice. The same kind of argument can be used to establish that, regardless of the lengths of the edges of a rectangle, the symmetry elements of it are the same and therefore there is only one rectangle lattice. Similarly there is only one lattice based on each of the rhombus, the hexagon, and the general parallelogram.

The assertion made earlier that there is only five plane lattices can now be seen to be an inevitable consequence of the existence of the various symmetry elements within them.

Chapter 5

Fractional Coordinates

It should be evident by now that while the diagrams in Figures 25, 26, 27, 30, and 32 show complete motifs at each lattice point of various primitive unit cells, not all of each motif lies entirely within any one particular cell. Careful consideration of these Figures shows that the parts of each motif that are actually located within one cell sum exactly to one whole motif. This summation is required by the definition of a primitive unit cell as one containing a single lattice point and therefore a single motif since the points are the sites of the motifs in the pattern.

It is now appropriate to examine the location in the cell of the motif or, if it happens to be complicated, the component parts of the motif.

First consider the simple case of a ◯ motif centred at each lattice point of a primitive unit cell, as shown in Figure 33(a). Since the unit cell is primitive it contains only one lattice point and, since there is one motif at each lattice point, the unit cell contains one motif. The two ways in which this single motif might be associated with the cell are shown in Figure 33(b), (c).

In (b) only that part of each motif that lies within the cell is shown; these parts clearly sum to one whole motif. The other parts of the four motifs are associated with the adjacent cells.

In (c) the whole of the motif at one point (A) is considered to belong to the cell ABCD even though not all of it lies within the cell. The motifs located at the other corners BCD are considered to belong to the appropriate adjacent unit cell. This method of representing the unit cell has three advantages over the method shown in (b). Firstly, the whole of the motif is shown at one site so that the size and shape of it are immediately evident. Secondly, it is only necessary to specify the location of the one whole motif and not the four parts, as would be required in (b). Thirdly, while the four parts of the divided (circular) motif for a square or rectangle unit cell are the same ($\alpha = 90°$), the four parts are considerably different for the general parallelogram, the rhombus, and the hexagon unit cells for which $\alpha \neq 90°$. For these reasons a plane pattern is invariably specified by the unit cell ABCD (whatever the size and shape may be), and a whole motif located at a representative point as shown in Figure 33(c).

It is now necessary to ask where the ◯ motif is located.

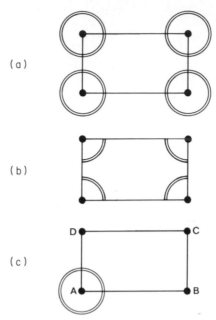

Figure 33. Diagrams showing: (a) a circular motif located at the points of a primitive rectangle unit cell; and the two ways, (b) and (c), of representing the single motif associated with the cell

At a corner of the unit cell?

At the lattice point of the unit cell?

Both answers while quite correct are not particularly informative and it is preferable to use an alternative prescription which provides meaningful information.

Consider the unit cell of the pattern shown in Figure 34(a). This unit cell is exactly the same as the cell shown in Figure 33(c) except that the motif is more complex consisting of ◯ plus ◯ .

It should be evident that to completely describe this pattern the location of both parts of the motif must be specified. To simply state that the ◯ is located at the corner of the cell or is centred upon the lattice point leaves the problem of specifying the location of the ◯ within the cell completely unanswered.

This problem is solved by using the centre c of the ◯ to locate it. Lines are

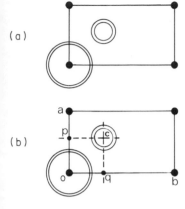

(a)

(b)

Figure 34. Diagrams showing: (a) a two-component circular motif associated with a lattice point of a unit cell; and (b) the construction for obtaining the fractional coordinates of that part of the motif located within the cell

drawn through c parallel to the edges of the cell as shown in Figure 34(b) and these intersect the edges at p and q. The lengths op ($= x$) and oq ($= y$) are the COORDINATES of the point c for the unit translations a and b intersecting at an origin o.

DEFINITION No. 15. THE COORDINATES OF ANY POINT IN A UNIT CELL ARE THE DISTANCES, MEASURED FROM THE ORIGIN TO THE INTERSECTIONS WITH THE EDGES, OF LINES DRAWN PARALLEL TO THEM THROUGH THE POINT.

Dividing the coordinates by the length of the appropriate unit translations produces the FRACTIONAL COORDINATES x/a and y/b. It is these numbers, the fractional coordinates, which are used to specify the location in the unit cell of the motif or the parts of the motif.

DEFINITION No. 16. THE FRACTIONAL COORDINATES OF ANY POINT WITHIN A UNIT CELL ARE THE COORDINATES OF THAT POINT REPRESENTED AS FRACTIONS OF THE UNIT TRANSLATIONS SPECIFYING THE EDGES OF THE UNIT CELL.

It should be appreciated now that the ⬡ part of the motif is preferably located by fractional coordinates and not be reference to the 'corner of the unit cell' or 'lattice point of the cell'. In this particular case the coordinates of the point at the centre of the large part of the motif are $x = 0$ and $y = 0$. Consequently the fractional coordinates of that point, i.e. the origin of the axes, are 0, 0. It should be noted that by convention the single lattice point associated with a primitive unit cell is located at the origin of the axes, i.e. at the site 0, 0. The points at the other corners of the cell and the motifs located at them are associated with the appropriate adjacent unit cells.

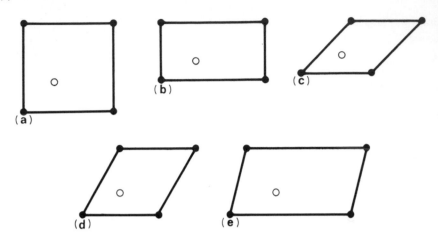

Figure 35. Unit cells of (a) the square, (b) the rectangle, (c) the rhombus, (d) the hexagon, and (e) the general parallelogram plane lattices showing the location in each of the point with fractional coordinates 1/3, 2/3 (origin at top left)

CONCEPT No. 27. THE MOTIF OR PART THEREOF LOCATED AT THE LATTICE POINT OF A PRIMITIVE UNIT CELL HAS THE FRACTIONAL COORDINATES 0, 0.

For a centred cell (see CONCEPT No. 17 and Figure 20(a), (b)), the lattice point at the geometrical centre of the cell is located at the site ½, ½ since the coordinates of the point are $a/2$, $b/2$ and the fractional coordinates are therefore $a/2a$ = ½, $b/2b$ = ½, i.e. ½, ½.

For the more complex non-primitive unit cells such as those shown in Figure 20(c), (d), (e), (f), the fractional coordinates of each lattice point within the cell are parameters which need to be specified in addition to the unit translations and the included angle to give a complete description of the cell.

It should be evident that equivalent points in all unit cells have identical fractional coordinates since these are simple ratios that are independent of the geometry of the cell. Figure 35 shows unit cells of each of the five plane lattices within which is located the point with fractional coordinates 1/3, 2/3. It is instructive to measure the unit translations a and b and the coordinates of the point for each cell to prove that the fractional coordinates of each of the points are indeed the same.

CONCEPT No. 28. THE FRACTIONAL COORDINATES OF A POINT WITHIN A UNIT CELL ARE INDEPENDENT OF THE ABSOLUTE VALUES OF THE UNIT TRANSLATIONS AND OF THE ANGLE BETWEEN THEM.

It is now possible to provide a complete description of the pattern shown by the

unit cell in Figure 34(a).
Unit cell parameters

$\mathbf{a} = 16$ mm,
$\mathbf{b} = 28$ mm,
$\alpha = 90°$,

motif 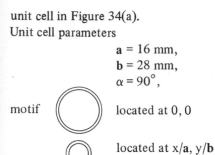   located at 0, 0

located at x/$\mathbf{a}$, y/$\mathbf{b}$
= 0.58, 0.32

This is precisely that information needed to construct the extended pattern, so that one of the objectives of the examination of plane lattices and patterns has now been achieved. This objective was to describe the pattern in such a way that the scheme of repetition, the nature of the motif, and the location of the motif in the unit cell be specified quantitatively with both precision and economy.

CONCEPT No. 29.   THE COMPLETE DESCRIPTION OF A PLANE PATTERN IS GIVEN BY THE PARAMETERS a, b, AND α OF THE UNIT CELL,   THE SIZE AND SHAPE OF THE MOTIF, AND THE FRACTIONAL COORDINATES LOCATING THE MOTIF (OR MOTIFS) WITHIN THE CELL.

It is now necessary to proceed to examine other properties of two-dimensional patterns and lattices.

Chapter 6

Indices in Plane Lattices

So far, in discussing two-dimensional patterns much has been made of the various sets of lines that pass through the points of the plane lattice. There is an infinite number of such sets, in general all having different spacing s and unit translation **t** (see Figure 12), and consequently being geometrically different. Every pair of such sets of lines defines a unit cell, primitive or non-primitive, which is representative of the lattice and also, of course, representative of the pattern.

Having selected that pair of sets of lines that defines the unit cell with simplest geometry in accordance with CONCEPT No. 16, it might be necessary for some purposes, as yet unspecified, to identify the lines so chosen. It might be also necessary to distinguish the other sets of lines which pass through the unit cell. Since all sets of lines are (generally) geometrically different, they can be differentiated and, if necessary, they can be identified as being different by some appropriate system of nomenclature.

In the case of the three-dimensional pattern of a crystal it is particularly necessary to identify specific DIRECTIONS and PLANES within the crystal. The reasons for this necessity will be examined in Chapter 19 but for the present it is sufficient to accept the necessity for a system to identify different directions and different planes and to see how this system can be obtained for the simple case of a two-dimensional pattern.

First however, what is meant by a DIRECTION and by a PLANE?

A direction is simply a straight line so that every set of lines through the points of a plane lattice (see Figure 12) identifies one direction in that lattice.

DEFINITION No. 17. A DIRECTION IS ANY LINE THROUGH THE POINTS OF A LATTICE.

As there is an infinite number of sets of lines in a plane lattice there is an infinite number of directions in a plane lattice, and, of course, an infinite number of directions in a plane pattern.

CONCEPT No. 30.   A PLANE PATTERN AND A PLANE LATTICE CONTAIN AN INFINITE NUMBER OF DIRECTIONS, ALL INFINITELY LONG.

Since a direction is simply a straight line, a direction in a two-dimensional pattern (or lattice) is in no way different from a direction in a three-dimensional pattern (or lattice), see DEFINITION No. 17. Consequently the system of nomenclature used to identify directions can be developed for the two-dimensional case and applied directly to the three-dimensional case without any difficulty. This will be demonstrated in the present chapter and later on in Chapter 19.

The consideration of directions will present no problems, but not so the consideration of planes.

A plane is a flat two-dimensional surface and clearly many planes exist in three-dimensional bodies. The sides of a box are planes and it should not be difficult to visualize other planes passing through a box.

In considering three-dimensional patterns, beginning in Chapter 8, it will be established that just as there is an infinite number of sets of lines through the points of a two-dimensional lattice, so there is an infinite number of sets of planes through the points of a three-dimensional lattice. This concept will be developed in Chapter 9 but for the moment it is sufficient to accept that the infinite number of planes does exist and that there are reasons why these planes need to be

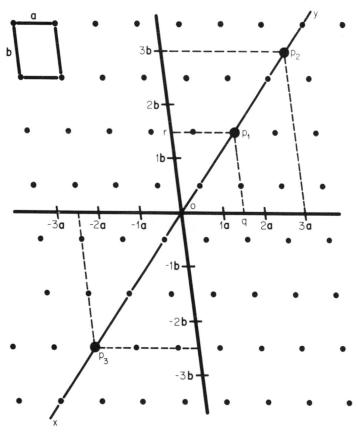

Figure 36. Part of a plane lattice with axes graduated in the unit translations a and b with direction xoy on which lie the points p_1, p_2, and p_3

distinguished one from the other. A system of nomenclature to identify them must be developed but a conceptual problem now arises. Although directions in two-dimensional and three-dimensional lattices are exactly the same, there is an obvious difficulty in trying to consider planes in this way as the concept of various 'planes' in two-dimensional lattices has no meaning. However, this really does not matter at all since the system that is used to identify the different planes in a three-dimensional lattice can be derived easily by the simple expedient of *imagining* that planes exist in two-dimensional lattices. The lines that pass through the points of such a lattice (see Figure 12) will be treated as 'planes' to devise the system to distinguish them, and this system will then apply directly to the actual planes in a three-dimensional lattice or pattern as will be seen in Chapter 19.

Although the systems which are used to identify the various directions and to identify the various planes are derived in somewhat different ways, both use a frame of reference consisting of the unit cell of the lattice or more specifically the edges of the unit cell, i.e. the unit translations.

Consider the plane lattice shown in Figure 36. Obviously the simplest unit cell (CONCEPT No. 16) which can be used to represent this lattice is the one shown at the top left corner of the diagram. This cell is derived from the unit translations a and b.

Next, note that two lines have been constructed, one parallel to the a unit translation of the unit cell, the other parallel to the b unit translation. These two lines are two directions in the lattice. They are the special directions parallel to the unit translations of the unit cell and as such are called the axes of the lattice.

DEFINITION No. 18. THE AXES OF A PLANE LATTICE ARE THE TWO SPECIAL LINES PARALLEL TO THE UNIT TRANSLATIONS OF THE UNIT CELL CHOSEN TO REPRESENT THE LATTICE.

It is preferable, but not necessary, for these axes to intersect either at a lattice point or better still, as shown in Figure 36, at the geometrical centre of a unit cell. Further, each axis is graduated with the appropriate unit translation and the graduation marks are labelled as shown. Note that the intersection of the axes becomes the origin o of the graduations, and that positive and negative senses from the origin along the axes are distinguished. These graduated axes are the frame of reference for identification both of directions and of 'planes' in the lattice.

Having now constructed the frame of reference it is relatively easy to discover how a direction can be identified. The line xoy passes through the origin, and is divided by the origin into two parts each of which is a direction. The part oy is regarded as commencing at the origin then passing through y and continuing to infinity. The part ox, opposite to oy, is similarly regarded as commencing at the origin then passing through x to infinity.

Consider first the direction oy.

The system used to identify this direction is developed by selecting any point such as p_1 on the direction then drawing lines through p_1 parallel to the axes. The intersections of these lines on the axes at q and r are the COORDINATES of the point p_1.

The coordinates are now expressed in terms of the unit translation graduations of the axes, i.e. q = +1.5a, and r = +1.5b, and written in the order:

+1.5a, +1.5b

The next step in identifying the direction oy is to divide each coordinate by the appropriate unit translation, i.e. divide the coordinate on the a axis by a and the coordinate on the b axis by b:

$$\frac{+1.5a}{a}, \frac{+1.5b}{b}$$

$$= 1.5, 1.5$$

This procedure eliminates the absolute values of the unit translations and the coordinates are now simple multiples of the distance used as the unit of measurement on each axis, i.e. the unit translations.

Finally the numbers (which being obtained by a division operation are the 'dividends') are made rational by conversion into integers (whole numbers) in the same ratio, usually the smallest numbers in that ratio. In the present case the integers are obtained by dividing by 1.5:

$$\frac{1.5}{1.5}, \frac{1.5}{1.5}$$

$$= 1, 1$$

These integers are termed the INDICES of the direction oy. By convention they are written in square brackets and without the comma, viz. [11]. The direction oy is the [11] direction (spoken: the one, one direction). The conventional use of square brackets signifies a particular direction.

DEFINITION No. 19. THE INDICES OF A DIRECTION ARE THOSE INTEGERS IN SQUARE BRACKETS THAT IDENTIFY THAT DIRECTION AND DISTINGUISH IT FROM ALL OTHERS.

The selection of some point other than p_1 on the direction oy for calculation of the indices results in exactly the same answer.

For example, for the point p_2:

coordinates	+ 3a, + 3b
divide by unit translations	$\frac{+3a}{a}, \frac{+3b}{b}$
	= 3, 3
rationalize the dividends	$\frac{3}{3}, \frac{3}{3}$
by dividing by 3	
	= 1, 1

and the indices of the direction are [11] as before.

For the opposite direction ox the same procedure is used, but a point such as p_3 must be chosen:

coordinates	$-2.5a, \quad -2.5b$
divide by unit translations	$\dfrac{-2.5a}{a}, \quad \dfrac{-2.5b}{b}$
	$= -2.5, \quad -2.5$
rationalize the dividends	$\dfrac{-2.5}{2.5}, \quad \dfrac{-2.5}{2.5}$
by dividing by 2.5	
	$= -1, \quad -1$

For this kind of solution in which negative numbers occur, the minus signs are always retained but are placed above the integers, not before them, and the indices so obtained are written in the conventional square brackets, viz. $[\bar{1}\bar{1}]$. The direction ox is the $[\bar{1}\bar{1}]$ direction (spoken: the bar one, bar one direction).

CONCEPT No. 31.   THE INDICES OF A DIRECTION ARE CALCULATED BY THE PROCEDURE:
   (A) MEASURE THE COORDINATES OF ANY POINT ON THE DIRECTION
   (B) DIVIDE THE COORDINATES BY THE APPROPRIATE UNIT TRANSLATIONS
   (C) RATIONALIZE THE DIVIDENDS,
   (D) PLACE THE RATIONALIZED DIVIDENDS IN SQUARE BRACKETS.

For the case just examined it will be noted that the direction ox is exactly opposite to the direction oy. Both have the same indices but with opposite signs on the indices. This is true of all pairs of directions which are the opposite senses of the same straight line bisected at the origin. For example, the opposite sense of the direction [12] is $[\bar{1}\bar{2}]$, of $[\bar{1}3]$ is $[1\bar{3}]$, of $[2\bar{5}]$ is $[\bar{2}5]$, and so on.

The same procedure for finding the indices of the directions [11] and $[\bar{1}\bar{1}]$ just described can be applied to all directions. Figure 37 shows some of the indexed directions, in the same lattice as shown in Figure 36, but note that in this diagram only one sense of most directions is shown. It is instructive to determine some of these indices using the method described in CONCEPT No. 31 and in particular to determine that the indices of the axes are [10], $[\bar{1}0]$, [01], and $[0\bar{1}]$.

There are three important points that should be clearly understood about this system of nomenclature for the identification of directions.

First, the indices do not depend on the actual lengths of the unit translations a and b. For example, the direction from the centre of a unit cell to one corner of the cell (direction oy in Figure 36) has the indices [11] for all values of a and b including the special case of $a = b$. Similarly all other particular directions in a unit

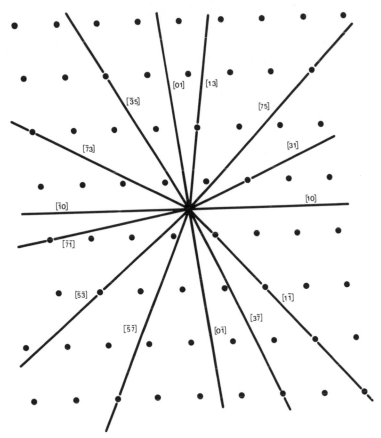

Figure 37. Diagram showing a few indexed directions in the plane lattice shown in Figure 36

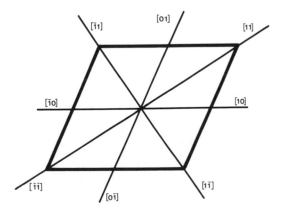

Figure 38. Some important directions in a general parallelogram unit cell

cell have the same indices for every combination of values of **a** and **b**. Secondly, the indices do not depend on the angle between the unit translations of the unit cell. The [11] direction has those same indices for all values of the angle between **a** and **b** including the special cases of $\alpha = 90°$ and $\alpha = 120°$. Similarly all other particular directions have the same indices for every value of α.

Thus, for all plane lattices the axes have the indices [10], [$\bar{1}$0], [01], [0$\bar{1}$]; the directions from the centre of the cell through the corners are [11], [$\bar{1}$1], [1$\bar{1}$], [$\bar{1}\bar{1}$], and so on as shown for the general parallelogram in Figure 38.

CONCEPT No. 32. THE INDICES OF DIRECTIONS IN A PLANE LATTICE
DO NOT DEPEND ON THE SIZE OR SHAPE OF THE
UNIT CELL SO THAT SIMILAR DIRECTIONS HAVE THE
SAME INDICES IN ALL LATTICES.

Thirdly, the indices of a direction can be determined if, and only if, that direction passes through the origin of the axes. This requirement presents no problems since a direction is simply one member of an infinite set of identical parallel lines and of this infinite set one line must necessarily pass through the origin as required. Refer to Figure 37 and the [31] direction just as an example. All lines parallel to this direction are also [31] directions even though they do not pass through the (selected) origin. Of course the parts of the lines of the set which are on the opposite side of the origin to the [31] direction have the opposite indices i.e. [$\bar{3}\bar{1}$].

So far only directions with specific indices have been considered but sometimes it is necessary to refer to a general direction rather than to a particular direction with particular indices. In this case the general indices [uv] are used.

CONCEPT No. 33. THE GENERAL INDICES [uv] REFER TO ANY
DIRECTION IN A PLANE PATTERN OR LATTICE.

It is now appropriate to turn to the more difficult problem of identifying 'planes'. The system which is used to distinguish a 'plane' is derived in a somewhat different way from the system used to distinguish a direction but uses the same frame of reference and the same kind of indices. The frame of reference is the graduated axes constructed in Figure 36 and shown again in Figure 39 together with single members from five different sets of lines, here treated as 'planes' to enable the system of nomenclature to be developed.

First consider the 'plane' labelled J and note that it intersects the axes at j and j'. These intersections are known as the INTERCEPTS of the plane on the axes. The intercepts are expressed in terms of the graduations along the axes, i.e. j = +2**a**, and j' = +3**b**, and are written in the order:

+2**a**, +3**b**

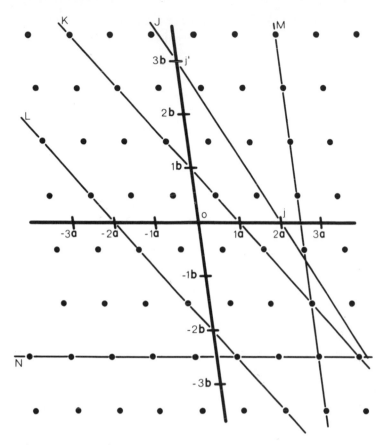

Figure 39. Part of a plane lattice with axes graduated in the unit translations **a** and **b** and planes J, K, L, M, and N

Next, divide by the unit translations (just as was done for directions):

$$\frac{+2a}{a}, \frac{+3b}{b}$$

$$= 2, 3$$

These dividends are now inverted; the reason for this step in the procedure will be explained in Chapter 19 but at the present it must simply be accepted that the inversion step is necessary in obtaining the indices for a plane. The inverted dividends are:

1/2, 1/3

Finally, the inverted dividends are rationalized by converting the fractions into integers in the same ratio. In the present case the rationalization is achieved by multiplying by 6:

$$6 \times 1/2, 6 \times 1/3$$
$$=3, 2$$

The integers are placed in round brackets without the comma and so the 'plane' J has the indices (32) – it is the (32) plane (spoken: the three, two plane). Round brackets are used by convention to signify a particular plane just as square brackets are used to signify a particular direction.

The 'plane' labelled K can be identified using the same procedure:

intercepts	1a, 1b
divide by unit translations	$\dfrac{1a}{a}, \dfrac{1b}{b}$
	$= 1, 1$
invert	$\dfrac{1}{1}, \dfrac{1}{1}$
	$= 1, 1$

rationalize – not required in this case.

The 'plane' K has the indices (11).

DEFINITION No. 20. THE INDICES OF A PLANE ARE THOSE INTEGERS IN ROUND BRACKETS THAT IDENTIFY THAT PLANE AND DISTINGUISH IT FROM ALL OTHERS.

The 'plane' labelled L is parallel to the 'plane' K but on the opposite side of the origin. Therefore, it would be expected to have the same indices as the 'plane' K except for reversal of the sign on each index. Thus the indices of the 'plane' L should be $(\bar{1}\bar{1})$ and this proves to be so as follows:

intercepts	$-2a, -2b$
divide by unit translations	$\dfrac{-2a}{a}, \dfrac{-2b}{b}$
	$= -2, -2$
invert	$-1/2, -1/2$
rationalize by multiplying by 2, remembering to always retain	$2 \times (-1/2), 2 \times (-1/2)$
the minus signs	$= -1, -1$

Thus, the 'plane' L does indeed have the indices $(\bar{1}\bar{1})$ as expected; the 'plane' L the $(\bar{1}\bar{1})$ 'plane' (spoken: the bar one, bar one plane).

Consider now the 'plane' M. The intercept on the a axis is clearly +2.5a, but what is the intercept on the b axis? Obviously the 'plane' M is parallel to the b axis and, by definition, parallel lines come together only at infinity. Therefore the 'plane' M intersects the **b** axis at infinity and so the intercept on the **b** axis is infinity. It is now simple to determine the indices:

intercepts	$+2.5\mathbf{a},\ \infty$
divide by unit translations	$\dfrac{+2.5\mathbf{a}}{\mathbf{a}},\ \dfrac{\infty}{\mathbf{b}}$
	$=\ 2.5,\infty$
invert	$1/2.5,\ 1/\infty$
rationalize by multiplying by 2.5,	
remembering that $1/\infty$ is zero	$2.5 \times 1/2.5,\ 2.5 \times 0$
	$=1,0$

The 'plane' M has the indices (10), and similarly the 'plane' N has indices (0$\bar{1}$) since it is parallel to the **a** axis.

CONCEPT No. 34.   THE INDICES OF A PLANE ARE CALCULATED BY THE PROCEDURE:
(A) MEASURE THE INTERCEPTS THAT THE PLANE MAKES ON THE AXES OF THE LATTICE,
(B) DIVIDE THE INTERCEPTS BY THE APPROPRIATE UNIT TRANSLATIONS,
(C) INVERT THE DIVIDENDS,
(D) RATIONALIZE THE INVERTED DIVIDENDS,
(E) PLACE THE RATIONALIZED NUMBERS IN ROUND BRACKETS.

There are three important points, very similar to those concerning the identification of directions, that should be understood about the system for identifying planes.

First, the indices do not depend on the actual lengths of the unit translations of the unit cell. The step (B) in the procedure described in CONCEPT No. 34 really prescribes that the intercepts be measured as multiples of the unit translations and so the unit of measurement along each axis is different for different unit translations. This ensures that equivalent 'planes' in different lattices have the same indices and thus the second point is that the indices are also independent of the angle between the unit translations.

CONCEPT No. 35.   THE INDICES OF 'PLANES' IN A PLANE LATTICE DO NOT DEPEND ON THE SIZE OR SHAPE OF THE UNIT CELL AND CONSEQUENTLY SIMILAR 'PLANES' HAVE THE SAME INDICES IN ALL LATTICES.

Thirdly, the indices of a 'plane' cannot be determined if the 'plane' passes through the origin of the axes. This restriction presents no problems since, for a particular location of the origin, only one 'plane' from each infinite set will pass through that origin; all others of the set will not pass through the origin and any one of them can be used to determine the indices. It should be noted that the 'planes' in the set are divided into two groups by the location of the origin. Both groups have the same indices but with opposite signs since the groups are on opposite sides of the origin.

Finally, just as it is sometimes necessary to specify a general direction by the general indices [uv], so it is sometimes necessary to specify a 'plane' without using particular indices. For such purposes the general indices (hk) are used.

CONCEPT No. 36.   THE GENERAL INDICES (hk) REFER TO ANY 'PLANE'
IN A PLANE LATTICE OR PATTERN.

Chapter 7

The Line Spacing

It has now been established that sets of indices, related to the axes selected to define the unit cell, can be calculated for each of the various directions and 'planes' in the plane lattice of a plane pattern.

Now one of the important properties of two-dimensional lattices examined in Chapter 2 was that each set of lines through the points of the lattice has a specific separation s, the line spacing, see Figure 12. Since each set of lines has identifying ('plane') indices and a particular value of s it is not surprising that a relationship exists between the two features. The relationship is provided by the parameters of the unit cell of the lattice, and will now be obtained for the case of the general parallelogram lattice by using the construction shown in Figure 40.

The only mathematics required for an understanding of the analysis is as follows.

(a) For any right-angled triangle ABC with sides a, b, and c:

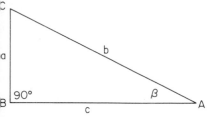

$\sin \beta = a/b$.

(b) For any triangle DEF:

$$\text{(i)} \quad \frac{\sin \alpha}{f} = \frac{\sin \beta}{d} = \frac{\sin \gamma}{e} \text{ , known as the sine rule;}$$

(ii) $f^2 = e^2 + d^2 - 2\,ed \cos \alpha$, known as the cosine rule.

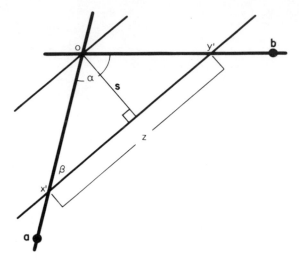

Figure 40. Diagram showing the construction for determining the s-spacing of a set of lines in a plane lattice specified by the unit translations **a** and **b** on axes intersecting at the origin o

Refer now to Figure 40 which shows the axes for a general parallelogram plane lattice with unit translations **a** and **b** and two adjacent members of some set of lines having the general indices for a 'plane' (hk). Note that one of the 'planes' passes through the origin so that the value of the line spacing s is measured from the origin o as shown.

The intercepts x (= ox′) and y (= oy′) of the 'plane' on the axes can be used to obtain the indices (hk) by the procedure described in CONCEPT No. 34:

intercepts	x, y
divide by unit translations	x/a, y/b
invert	a/x, b/y

Therefore, the index $h = a/x$ and the index $k = b/y$, so that $x = a/h$ and $y = b/k$ or $x^2 = a^2/h^2$ and $y^2 = b^2/k^2$ for use later in the analysis.

Application of the sine rule to Figure 40 results in the equation

$$\frac{\sin \alpha}{z} = \frac{\sin \beta}{y}$$

and since $\sin \beta = s/x$

$$\frac{\sin \alpha}{z} = \frac{s}{xy}$$

so that

$$\frac{1}{s} = \frac{z}{xy \sin \alpha}$$

nd

$$\frac{1}{s^2} = \frac{z^2}{x^2 y^2 \sin^2 \alpha}$$

Now, from the cosine rule

$$z^2 = y^2 + x^2 - 2xy \cos \alpha$$

o that

$$\frac{1}{s^2} = \frac{y^2 + x^2 - 2xy \cos \alpha}{x^2 y^2 \sin^2 \alpha}$$

nd so

$$\frac{1}{s^2} = \frac{1}{x^2 \sin^2 \alpha} + \frac{1}{y^2 \sin^2 \alpha} - \frac{2 \cos \alpha}{xy \sin^2 \alpha}$$

Substituting for x, x^2, y, and y^2 produces the most useful form of the relationship between the spacing s, the indices (hk), and the parameters $\mathbf{a}$, $\mathbf{b}$, and α for this lattice. Thus for the GENERAL PARALLELOGRAM:

$$\frac{1}{s^2} = \frac{h^2}{a^2 \sin^2 \alpha} + \frac{k^2}{b^2 \sin^2 \alpha} - \frac{2hk \cos \alpha}{ab \sin^2 \alpha}$$

This equation can be used as a basis to obtain equivalent relationships for the other four plane lattices.

RHOMBUS: $\mathbf{a} = \mathbf{b}$ and the equation becomes

$$\frac{1}{s^2} = \frac{h^2 + k^2 - 2hk \cos \alpha}{a^2 \sin^2 \alpha}$$

HEXAGON: $\mathbf{a} = \mathbf{b}$, $\alpha = 120°$, $\cos \alpha = -1/2$, $\sin \alpha = \sqrt{3}/2$, and the equation becomes

$$\frac{1}{s^2} = \frac{4(h^2 + k^2 + hk)}{3a^2}$$

RECTANGLE: $\alpha = 90°$, $\cos \alpha = 0$, $\sin \alpha = 1$, and the equation becomes

$$\frac{1}{s^2} = \frac{h^2}{a^2} + \frac{k^2}{b^2}$$

SQUARE: $\mathbf{a} = \mathbf{b}$, $\alpha = 90°$, $\cos \alpha = 0$, $\sin \alpha = 1$ and the equation becomes

$$\frac{1}{s^2} = \frac{h^2 + k^2}{a^2}$$

These relationships can be used to calculate the separation s of the sets of lines that can be drawn through the points of any plane lattice. The only condition imposed on the calculation is that the indices of the lines be determined using the procedure given in CONCEPT No. 34 which treats the lines in the same way as planes.

CONCEPT No. 37.   FOR EACH PLANE LATTICE THERE EXISTS A
                   PARTICULAR RELATIONSHIP BETWEEN THE
                   SEPARATION s OF THE SETS OF LINES IN THE
                   LATTICE, THE INDICES OF THE LINES (TREATED AS
                   PLANES), AND THE PARAMETERS OF THE UNIT CELL.

The way in which these relationships might be used can be demonstrated by a simple problem.

What is the separation of the (32) lines ('planes') in a pattern with the rectangle unit cell specified by $a = 20$ mm, $b = 50$ mm?

Solution: for the rectangle unit cell

$$\frac{1}{s^2} = \frac{h^2}{a^2} + \frac{k^2}{b^2}$$

so that substituting for a, b, h, and k gives

$$\frac{1}{s^2} = \frac{3^2}{20^2} + \frac{2^2}{50^2}$$

$$= \frac{9}{400} + \frac{4}{2500}$$

$$= 0.0225 + 0.0016$$

$$= 0.0241$$

so that

$$s^2 = 1/0.0241$$

$$= 41.5$$

and

$$s = 6.44 \text{ mm}$$

Although a problem such as this appears to be trivial for two-dimensional lattices it has considerable relevance to the determination of the structure of crystals as will be seen in Chapter 22.

The basic introduction to the structure and geometrical properties of patterns in two dimensions has now been completed. The 20 DEFINITIONS and 37 CONCEPTS stating the principles of importance will be extended in the next chapters to provide the framework for understanding the structure and properties of the three-dimensional pattern of a crystal.

Chapter 8

Crystals

In the first part of this book it was shown that a motif and a plane lattice can be assembled to produce a plane pattern. Such patterns are quite familiar, for man, although a three-dimensional creature, finds it necessary to surround himself with two-dimensional surfaces. Many of these surfaces are adorned with repetitive designs particularly on the clothes that he wears and on the buildings he inhabits. The patterns are developed by the very process that has just been used to arrive at an understanding of them – the putting together of the two parts, the motif and the lattice that specifies the scheme of repetition.

It is difficult to identify a two-dimensional pattern that has not been made artificially in this way as there are very few such patterns that occur in nature. On the other hand, it is just as difficult to identify an example of a three-dimensional pattern which is not a naturally occurring phenomenon – man has had little occasion actually to construct patterns in three dimensions.

One of the most important three-dimensional patterns in nature occurs in the solids with which this book is concerned – crystals – and just as plane patterns consist of a motif and a lattice so also does the three-dimensional pattern of a crystal consist of a motif and a lattice.

Crystals have a motif that is composed of one or more atoms and, being a creation of nature, it is inappropriate to adopt the approach of 'assembling' a crystal from a motif and a lattice. However, this in no way detracts from the concepts of the motif and the lattice since the pattern of a crystal does not differ from the pattern of a carpet (for example), in any significant way. The two patterns are distinguished only by the additional dimension in the crystal and the considerable difference in the sizes of the motifs and the schemes of repetition. The two kinds of pattern are basically the same with basically the same geometrical properties.

The first question that must be answered before the pattern of a crystal can be examined in any detail is 'what exactly is a crystal?'.

It is possible to answer this question in quite general terms for a vast amount of information concerning crystals has been accumulated since the discovery in 1912 that X-rays can be used to study the arrays of atoms within them. This discovery gave access to what was previously a totally unexplored part of nature and subsequently man developed an insatiable curiosity about crystalline substances and, to satisfy that curiosity, devised the techniques to inquire experimentally into the intricacies of the crystal. As a result of these inquiries he has learnt that crystals are one of the most exquisite of all natural phenomena.

After the innumerable studies that these techniques made possible it is now known with complete certainty that a crystal is a solid in which the component atoms occur in a three-dimensional periodic array — the atoms or groups of atoms or molecules form an orderly repetitive pattern.

DEFINITION No. 21. A CRYSTAL IS A SOLID IN WHICH THE COMPONENT ATOMS OCCUR IN A REPETITIVE THREE-DIMENSIONAL ARRAY.

A crystal is a pattern in three dimensions and any solid which has this property is said to be CRYSTALLINE. A crystalline solid which consists of only one crystal is called a SINGLE CRYSTAL. Examples of single crystals are the gemstones diamond, sapphire, ruby, a prism of quartz, a single sheet of mica, a crystal of alum or copper sulphate grown from a saturated solution, a cube of table salt, a snowflake, and so on.

DEFINITION No. 22. A SINGLE CRYSTAL IS AN ISOLATED PIECE OF ONE CRYSTAL OF A CRYSTALLINE SOLID.

On the other hand a crystalline solid may be composed of many crystals and this kind of solid is said to be POLYCRYSTALLINE. The crystals in a polycrystalline solid — a POLYCRYSTAL — are generally called GRAINS. These grains are interlocked and in contact with one another at the GRAIN BOUNDARIES to form a void-free, coherent mass. The grains (individual crystals) might be all the same kind as in gold or marble or quartzite or washing soda or rock salt, or might consist of two or more different kinds as in granite or pegmatite or concrete or steel.

However, regardless of whether the crystals in a polycrystal are all the same kind or a mixture of different kinds, each one of them is a true crystal, being composed of a regular three-dimensional array of atoms just as in an isolated single crystal. It is only the state of aggregation that distinguishes a polycrystal from a single crystal.

DEFINITION No. 23. A POLYCRYSTAL IS AN AGGREGATE OF CRYSTALS (GRAINS), WHICH MIGHT OR MIGHT NOT BE OF DIFFERENT KINDS, GENERALLY IRREGULARLY SHAPED AND INTERLOCKED TOGETHER AT THE BOUNDARIES OF CONTACT.

Having now reached an elementary understanding of the nature of the crystalline state in terms of the DEFINITIONS Nos. 21, 22, and 23 it is possible to begin to inquire into some of the properties of the pattern of the regular array of atoms that comprise a crystal.

The analysis of the various qualities, features, and properties of two-dimensional patterns provided a number of concepts and definitions which will now be used to examine the structure of crystals by taking each in turn and seeing how it applies to the three-dimensional case. Consider the very first concept.

CONCEPT No. 1.   A PLANE PATTERN CONSISTS OF A MOTIF REPEATED ACCORDING TO A SCHEME OF REPETITION.

A crystal, whether it exists in isolation or in a polycrystal, is a three-dimensional pattern of atoms and consequently it is possible to distinguish the motif and the scheme whereby the motif is repeated in space to generate the pattern.

The motif of a crystal depends upon the chemical identity of the material of the crystal but can be only a single atom, a group of atoms, a single molecule, or a group of molecules. This analysis will not be concerned with either the number of atoms or molecules in the motif or the arrangement of them in the motif until Chapter 15, but examples of crystals having a motif of these various kinds are:

single atom:	many metallic elements such as copper, silver, gold, iron, nickel, and so on;
group of atoms:	other elements such as zinc, iodine, sulphur, cadmium, manganese, diamond, and graphite;
single molecule:	caesium chloride, titanium carbide, sodium chloride (rock salt, common salt or table salt), lead sulphide (galena), zinc sulphide (zinc blende), calcium fluoride (fluorite), epsom salts, and many others;
group of molecules:	iron carbide (cementite), rutile, zircon, silicon carbide, and potassium cyanide, to mention a few.

Since the three-dimensional pattern of a crystal is geometrically similar to a two-dimensional plane pattern, CONCEPT No. 1 can be restated as follows.

CONCEPT No. 38.   THE THREE-DIMENSIONAL PATTERN OF A CRYSTAL HAS TWO COMPONENT PARTS, THE MOTIF AND THE SCHEME OF REPETITION.

Now in the three-dimensional pattern of a crystal, the motif, whatever it may be, is repeated periodically in space, so that the scheme of repetition describing this periodicity must be represented in much the same way as the scheme of repetition is represented for a plane pattern. It has been established that

CONCEPT No. 2.   The scheme of repetition of a pattern is specified by an array of points

— which for a plane pattern is two-dimensional. Therefore, it follows that the scheme of repetition of the pattern of a crystal must be represented by an array of points in three dimensions.

CONCEPT No. 39.   THE SCHEME OF REPETITION FOR THE MOTIF IN THE
PATTERN OF A CRYSTAL IS REPRESENTED BY A
THREE-DIMENSIONAL ARRAY OF POINTS.

The relationship between each point in the scheme and the motif it represents is specified by CONCEPT No. 3.

CONCEPT No. 3.   Every point in the scheme of repetition must bear exactly
the same relationship to the motif it represents.

This concept is quite general, being a requirement for patterns in any number of dimensions. It was seen in Chapter 1 that the concept was true for the case of the two-dimensional pattern and it is equally true for the patterns that are now being considered — the three-dimensional pattern of a crystal. Every point in the array of points that constitutes the scheme of repetition bears exactly the same relationship to the associated motif as does every other point in the array. The perfection specified in CONCEPT No. 3 was shown to require the following.

CONCEPT No. 4.   Perfect patterns and the associated array of points showing
the scheme of repetition extend to infinity.

While this concept is certainly true in principle and while it might be easily imagined that a plane pattern can be as extensive as the plane on which it occurs, even infinite, there is no possible way in which the three-dimensional pattern of a crystal can be infinite. An infinite crystal is beyond conception as it would fill all space. In fact rather than being immense objects, crystals are generally very small. Certainly a few mineral crystals with masses of many thousands of kilograms have been found but usually crystals have a mass that is a fraction of a kilogram and a volume of perhaps a cubic millimetre or so.

However, it would be a mistake to be too hasty for it is most instructive to consider a crystal with the size of a pin head, that is, a crystal with a volume of about one cubic millimetre and to ask 'how many motifs does such a crystal contain?' As will be seen later, the distance between motifs in a crystal is typically 300 picometre (pm) where $1 \text{ pm} = 10^{-12} \text{ m}$ or 10^{-9} mm and $100 \text{ pm} = 1$ Ångstrom unit (Å), the new obsolete unit of measurement. It is easy to calculate that, if the crystal is divided into cubes, each cube containing one motif, the volume of these small cubes would be $3 \times 3 \times 3 \times 10^{-21}$ cubic millimetres (mm^3). Thus the volume associated with each motif is $27 \times 10^{-21} \text{ mm}^3$. The inverse of this volume is the number of motifs in each cubic millimetre of crystal; this number is $1/(27 \times 10^{-21})$ or approximately 10^{20}. Thus, a crystal having the size of a pin head contains 10^{20} motifs; this number 10^{20} is written in long notation as 100,000,000,000,000,000,000 which is one hundred million million million. A very large number.

How large a carpet square would be needed to accommodate the same number of motifs?

The usual kind of carpet pattern has motifs that are about one metre apart, that is, on each square metre of carpet there is one motif of the pattern. Thus, it is evident that to contain 10^{20} motifs the area of the carpet would need to be 10^{20} square metres which means that the edge length of the square would be 10^{10} metres. How far is 10^{10} metres? Well, one megametre (Mm) is 1,000,000 metres so that the edge of the carpet square would be 10,000 megametres long and since the earth is 12.8 megametres in diameter a carpet square of the required size is almost inconceivable. The edge length is in fact rather more than twenty-five times the distance from the earth to the moon. From the point of view of the size of earthly objects such a carpet square must surely be immensely large and, this being the case, then the pin head size crystal also must be immensely large from the point of view of the size and separation of the motifs (atoms) it contains.

If this argument and conclusion is accepted, then the assertion in CONCEPT. No 4 that patterns extend to infinity now makes some sense even when applied to the smallest of crystals and the analogue may be written as follows.

CONCEPT No. 40.   CRYSTALS ARE IMMENSELY LARGE WHEN COMPARED WITH THE SIZE OF THE ATOMS IN THE MOTIF.

Chapter 9

Space Lattices

Having now established that a crystal consists of a motif and a scheme of repetition represented by a three-dimensional array of points it is appropriate to proceed as in Chapter 2 to consider the properties of this array.

Even though it has just been shown that compared with the size of the atoms in the motif a crystal is immensely large, the array of points in the associated scheme of repetition must be infinitely large as a consequence of CONCEPT No. 5.

CONCEPT No. 5.   The points in the array showing the scheme of repetition of a pattern are indistinguishable from one another.

This concept, it will be remembered, was derived from the property of a pattern that the motifs repeat with regular periodicity according to the scheme of repetition. Just as this means that the array of points for a plane pattern can have no boundaries, otherwise the points on the edge would be distinguishable from those in the interior (see Figure 10), so it also means that the three-dimensional array of points for a crystal can have no boundaries for exactly the same reasons. By DEFINITION No. 1, an infinite array of indistinguishable points in a plane is a plane lattice and it follows that an infinite array of indistinguishable points in three dimensions is also called a lattice, in this case a SPACE LATTICE.

DEFINITION No. 24. A SPACE LATTICE IS AN INFINITE ARRAY OF POINTS
IN THE THREE DIMENSIONS OF SPACE SUCH THAT
EVERY POINT IS ABSOLUTELY INDISTINGUISHABLE
FROM EVERY OTHER POINT.

For the lattice points to be indistinguishable from one another every point must have exactly the same surroundings in exactly the same orientation. This requirement was demonstrated in Figure 11 for the two-dimensional case. Further, the space lattice must be perfect since any defect in the array would provide a means of distinguishing those points near the defect from those points far away and the points of a space lattice are the LATTICE POINTS as defined in DEFINITION No. 2.

DEFINITION No. 2.   A lattice point is any point of a lattice.

It was shown by CONCEPT No. 6 that the plane lattice is that particular array of points showing the scheme of repetition for a two-dimensional pattern.

CONCEPT No. 6.   The plane lattice of a two-dimensional pattern is that array of points which specifies the scheme of repetition of the pattern.

The same kind of concept applies to three-dimensional patterns except that for this case it is the space lattice that specifies the scheme.

CONCEPT No. 41.   THE SPACE LATTICE OF A CRYSTAL IS THAT ARRAY OF POINTS WHICH SPECIFIES THE SCHEME OF REPETITION OF THE PATTERN OF THE CRYSTAL.

Thus, it is seen that the pattern of a crystal can be represented by the atom or group of atoms or molecules comprising the motif and the space lattice which specifies the scheme whereby the motif is repeated periodically in the three dimensions of space. The combination of the space lattice and the motif defines exactly that three-dimensional array of atoms which constitutes a crystal and which is called the CRYSTAL STRUCTURE.

DEFINITION No. 25.   THE CRYSTAL STRUCTURE OF ANY CRYSTALLINE SOLID IS THAT PARTICULAR THREE-DIMENSIONAL ARRAY OF ATOMS OF WHICH THE SOLID IS COMPOSED AND WHICH IS SPECIFIED BY THE MOTIF AND THE SPACE LATTICE.

Before it is possible to explore various crystal structures it is necessary to examine closely the properties of space lattices just as the properties of plane lattices were explored.   Part of a space lattice is shown in Figure 41. Remember that space lattices extend to infinity in all directions so that the diagram shows only a very small portion of the lattice and the bounding surfaces are included solely for clarity. One way to form a mental conception of this lattice is to visualize it as a stack of parallel identical plane lattices — that is to identify a set of parallel planes, equally spaced, that pass through the points of the lattice. For the purposes of studying the properties of crystals a plane is defined as follows.

DEFINITION No. 26.   A PLANE IS ANY FLAT TWO-DIMENSIONAL SURFACE OF POINTS OF A SPACE LATTICE.

However, as is indicated by the diagram shown in Figure 42, there is a number of ways in which such planes may be seen to exist. Parts of four sets of different planes are shown but since the lattice is infinite in extent the number of different sets of planes that occur in it must also be infinite.

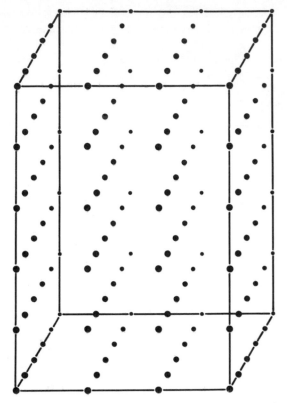

Figure 41. Part of a three-dimensional array of points of a space lattice

CONCEPT No. 42.   AN INFINITE NUMBER OF SETS OF EQUALLY SPACED PARALLEL PLANES EXIST THROUGH THE POINTS OF A SPACE LATTICE.

Any one of this infinity of sets may be regarded as the stack of parallel plane lattices referred to previously and which have the property specified in CONCEPT No. 7.

CONCEPT No. 7.   The points of a lattice occur in sets of straight lines.

Thus, lines occur through the points of each of the planes in any set and therefore, of course, through the points of all possible sets of planes. Clearly, then CONCEPT No. 7 is quite general and lines occur through the points of a plane lattice and through the points of a space lattice. The total number of sets of lines that occur through the points of a space lattice is specified by the general CONCEPT No. 9.

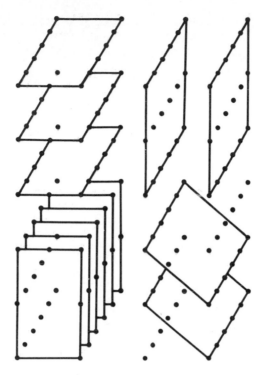

Figure 42. Part of a space lattice showing portions of four different sets of planes through the points

CONCEPT No. 9.   An infinite number of different sets of lines occur through the points of any lattice.

It has been seen that these sets of lines have the special property described by CONCEPT No. 8.

CONCEPT No. 8.   The sets of lines of points in a lattice are characterized by a spacing, s, and a point separation, t, the product of which, (s x t), is a constant for the lattice, and $1/(s \times t)$ is the number, N, of lattice points per unit area.

The idea embodied in this concept is that the distribution of points in a plane lattice is not dependent on the way in which the sets of lines occur. The same principle is equally relevant to a space lattice but not in quite the same form. For space lattices it is far more useful to direct attention to the sets of planes that pass through the lattice points rather than the lines through them. All planes in a set are equally spaced and the perpendicular separation **d** is called the **d**-SPACING or the **d**-VALUE.

DEFINITION No. 27. THE d-SPACING OF ANY SET OF PLANES THROUGH
THE POINTS OF A SPACE LATTICE IS THE PERPEN-
DICULAR DISTANCE BETWEEN ANY TWO ADJACENT
PLANES IN THE SET.

As every particular set of planes contains a particular density of points N, the number of points per unit area − see CONCEPT No. 8 − then the product of N and the inverse of the d-spacing for that set of planes is the number of points in a unit volume of the space lattice. This number must be a constant for the lattice and so must be independent of that particular set of planes chosen to make the calculation. Thus the product $N \times (1/d)$ is the density of points in the space lattice and must have the same value for all sets of planes. It will be appreciated that the density of points in a plane N is $1/(s \times t)$ as specified in CONCEPT No. 8 which can now be extended to the following.

CONCEPT No. 43.   THE PLANES OF A SPACE LATTICE HAVE A DENSITY
OF POINTS $N = 1/(s \times t)$, AND ARE CHARACTERIZED
BY A SEPARATION d SUCH THAT THE PRODUCT
$N \times (1/d) = 1/(s \times t \times d)$ IS A CONSTANT, BEING THE
DENSITY OF POINTS IN THE SPACE LATTICE.

The separation t of points in any line is the unit translation for that line as previously defined.

DEFINITION No. 3.   A unit translation is the distance between adjacent points
along any line in a lattice.

Since there is an infinite number of sets of lines in a space lattice there is also an infinite number of different unit translations in a space lattice. This concept, in general form, was established in CONCEPT No. 10.

CONCEPT No. 10   There is an infinite number of unit translations in every
lattice.

For the case of the plane lattice it was seen that a unit cell of the lattice could be constructed from every pair of different unit translations.

DEFINITION No. 4.   A unit cell of a plane lattice is a parallelogram of two unit
translations with lattice points at the corners and is perfectly
representative of the lattice.

Note that this definition does not preclude the possibility that the unit cell may contain additional lattice points, i.e. that it may be non-primitive.

The lines corresponding to the unit translations chosen to specify the unit cell divide the plane lattice into an infinity of unit cells as shown in Figure 14. These cells are parallelograms and each one, being identical with every other one, is a completely representative part of the lattice. The concept of the unit cell as a small representative part of the lattice also applies to three-dimensional space lattices but in this case, to be representative, the cell must be necessarily three dimensional. There are two ways in which the subdivision of a space lattice into unit cells can be imagined.

As was seen in CONCEPT No. 9 there is an infinite number of different sets of lines, each line infinitely long, through the points of any lattice, or, to be specific, any space lattice. Every combination of three sets of these lines divides the lattice into small volumes such as each of those shown in Figure 43. Of course it is necessary that the three sets of lines do not all lie in the same plane. The small volume obtained from the intersection of three sets of lines is the three-dimensional analogue of the two-dimensional parallelogram. This volume is a six-sided polyhedron for which each side is a parallelogram and opposite sides are identical. Such a polyhedron is called a parallelepiped and so the unit cell of a space lattice is a parallelepiped.

The alternative approach to the identification of the unit cell of a space lattice is based on the CONCEPT No. 42 that there is an infinite number of sets of planes through the points of the lattice. Since the planes in any set are equally spaced and infinite in extent, any one set of planes divides the lattice into an infinite number

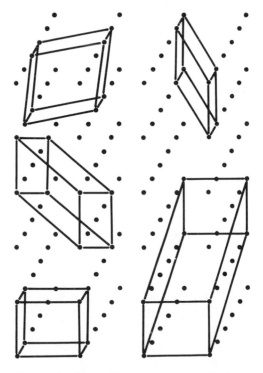

Figure 43. Five different unit cells in a space lattice

of identical slabs, infinite in extent, but with thickness equal to the separation of the planes, i.e. to the d-spacing of the planes. A second set of planes, different from the first set, divides the slabs into identical strips, each strip being infinitely long with thickness equal to the d-spacing of the first set of planes and width equal to the d-spacing of the second set. Finally, a third set of planes divides the strips into identical parallelepipeds with depth equal to the d-spacing of that third set. So, it is seen that any three sets of planes divide a space lattice into small volumes each of which is an identical parallelepiped again, such as any of those shown for example in Figure 43. Thus, it is possible to obtain exactly the same unit cell from the intersection of three different sets of planes or the intersection of three different sets of non-coplanar lines and obviously some relationship between the sets of planes and the sets of lines must exist. This relationship can be seen by inspection of the unit cells shown in Figure 43 which clearly demonstrates for any particular cell the three sets of lines lie at the intersections of the three sets of planes.

The number of unit cells obtained from either three sets of lines or three sets of planes is necessarily infinite since all space lattices are infinite in extent. Each unit cell is identical with every other unit cell formed from the same three sets of lines or the same three sets of planes. Consequently any one of the cells can be used to generate the whole lattice by repetition of it in the three dimensions of space. In the simplest case the unit cell has lattice points only at the corners but additional points within the cell also may be present. This feature will be examined in detail in Chapter 13 but now it is only important to realize that all unit cells have lattice points at least at the corners so that the lengths of the edges of the cell must be the separation of points along the lines that define the edges. These separations are, of course, the unit translations of the particular lines.

DEFINITION No. 28. A UNIT CELL OF A SPACE LATTICE IS A PARALLELEPIPED HAVING THREE NON-COPLANAR UNIT TRANSLATIONS AS EDGES AND IS REPRESENTATIVE OF THE LATTICE.

Since there is an infinite number of different unit translations there is an infinite number of different ways in which three of them can be combined together and therefore there is an infinite number of different unit cells for every lattice. Equivalently, there is an infinite number of different ways of selecting three sets of planes in a space lattice to produce a unit cell so that the CONCEPT No. 11 has quite general application.

CONCEPT No. 11.   There is an infinite number of different unit cells which can be used to describe any lattice.

Thus, to specify the structure of a crystal, it is necessary to define the size and shape of a unit cell, the location in it of the lattice points, and the array of atoms in the motif located at each lattice point. It is now necessary to discover how to define the size and shape of the unit cell.

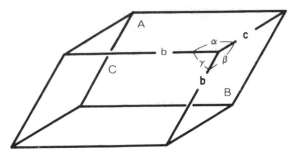

Figure 44. Diagram showing that the parameters **a**, **b**, **c**, α, β, and γ specify the size and shape of the parallelepiped unit cell of a space lattice

For the case of a two-dimensional lattice it was seen in CONCEPT No. 12 that the unit cell is completely specified by the lengths of the two edges (the unit translations), and the angle between them. Since in the three-dimensional space lattice the unit cell is a parallelepiped, it must be specified in a similar way by the lengths of the three edges (the unit translations) and the angles between them. Thus the unit translations **a**, **b**, and **c** and the included angles α, β, and γ shown in Figure 44 provide all the information necessary to completely describe the size and shape of the cell.

CONCEPT No. 44.   A UNIT CELL OF A SPACE LATTICE IS COMPLETELY SPECIFIED BY THE UNIT TRANSLATIONS a, b, AND c, AND THE ANGLES α, β, AND γ BETWEEN THEM.

The three unit translations and three included angles which specify the size and shape of the unit cell are the LATTICE PARAMETERS as defined below.

DEFINITION No. 5.   The lattice parameters of a unit cell are those unit translations and angles which must be assigned values to specify the dimensions of the cell.

By convention, the unit translations are usually labelled as a 'right handed' set such that rotation from **a** to **b** would drive **c** in the direction of a right-handed screw. Also by convention, the angles between the unit translations are labelled as follows:

α is between **b** and **c**,
β is between **c** and **a**, and
γ is between **a** and **b**.

Further, the faces of the unit cell are labelled as:

the A face with **b** and **c** as edges and containing angle α,
the B face with **a** and **c** as edges and containing angle β, and
the C face with **a** and **b** as edges and containing angle γ.

These features of the unit cell are shown in the diagram in Figure 44.

It was seen in Chapter 3 that it is useful to classify the plane lattices into a small number of different kinds according to the shape of the unit cell.

CONCEPT No. 13.   There are five different plane lattices.

Similarly it is possible and indeed most useful and desirable to classify space lattices into a small number of different kinds. The usefulness of this classification lies in the means it provides for classifying crystals and obtaining information about the properties that crystals possess.

The number of basically different kinds of schemes of repetition — space lattices — for crystals must be the same as the number of different ways in which the representative unit cell can occur. This is clearly the number of different ways in which it is possible to construct a parallelepiped and happens to be seven. Why the number should be seven is best explained not by considering the unit cell as was the procedure adopted for the case of the plane lattice, but rather by examining the symmetry properties of space lattices and it is appropriate to now proceed in this way.

Chapter 10

Macroscopic Symmetry

In considering the symmetry properties of plane lattices and plane patterns it was seen that there are several symmetry operations which transform an appropriate body to self coincidence.

DEFINITION No. 8.   A symmetry operation is any operation that can be performed on a body to transform it to self coincidence.

Also remembering

CONCEPT No. 18.   Two or more positions of a body that are indistinguishable from one another are self coincident positions.

The various kinds of symmetry operations that can occur in three-dimensional patterns and in space lattices include all the operations described in Chapter 4 for the plane lattice and pattern.

Thus, space lattices or crystals may have rotational symmetry about some axis as defined below.

DEFINITION No. 10. An axis is any line in a pattern or lattice that serves a useful purpose in specifying the properties of that pattern or lattice.

A rotation axis is defined as follows.

DEFINITION No. 9.   A rotation axis of symmetry is any line about which a body may be rotated to one or more positions of self coincidence.

Further, the quality of a rotation axis is specified by DEFINITION No. 11.

DEFINITION No. 11. An N-fold rotation axis of symmetry is a line about which a body is transformed to self coincidence N times during a 360° rotation. The angle θ between the self coincident positions is 360°/N.

Rotation of a space lattice about any line (an axis) may transform the lattice to self coincidence 1, 2, 3, 4, or 6 times during a full 360°. Most arbitrary axes are

76

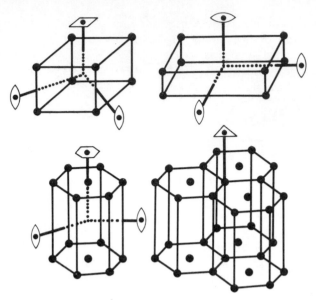

Figure 45. Diagrams showing the locations of various kinds of rotation axes that occur in three different space lattices

1-fold axes, that is, the lattice is in self coincident positions only at the beginning and completion of the 360° rotation. However, there may exist a few special axes about which rotation through a full circle results in 2, 3, 4, or 6 positions of self coincidence. Examples of such axes, identified by the appropriate symbols (see Chapter 4), are shown in Figure 45.

Thus the only rotation axes that can occur in space lattices are:

1-fold: symbol 1
2-fold: symbol 2
3-fold: symbol 3
4-fold: symbol 4
6-fold: symbol 6

Other kinds of rotational symmetry such as 5-fold, 7-fold, and higher order axes are impossible, being incompatible with a parallelepiped unit cell and so

CONCEPT No. 19: Plane lattices have at least 2-fold, 3-fold, 4-fold, or 6-fold rotation axes of symmetry

is extended to CONCEPT No. 45.

CONCEPT No. 45. SPACE LATTICES HAVE 1-FOLD, 2-FOLD, 3-FOLD, 4-FOLD, OR 6-FOLD AXES OF ROTATIONAL SYMMETRY.

Note that while a plane lattice necessarily has at least a 2-fold rotation axis through the centre of the unit cell, it is possible for a three-dimensional space lattice to contain only 1-fold axes.

The rotational symmetry of a space lattice of a particular crystal is not necessarily the same as the rotational symmetry of the crystal itself, as follows from CONCEPT No. 20.

CONCEPT No. 20.   The rotational symmetry of a plane pattern depends not only on the rotational symmetry of the lattice but also on the shape of the motif.

If the motif has a lower rotational symmetry than has the lattice then the rotational symmetry of the pattern is correspondingly lower. This concept is true for patterns in both two and three dimensions so that

CONCEPT No. 21.   Plane patterns contain 1-fold, 2-fold, 3-fold, 4-fold or 6-fold axes of rotational symmetry

can be extended to the pattern of a crystal.

CONCEPT No. 46.   CRYSTALS CONTAIN 1-FOLD, 2-FOLD, 3-FOLD, 4-FOLD OR 6-FOLD AXES OF ROTATIONAL SYMMETRY.

Alternatively, if the motif has higher rotational symmetry than has the lattice, the rotational symmetry of the pattern is NOT increased and, as was shown in Figure 27, the rotational symmetry may even be reduced. Thus

CONCEPT No. 22.   The highest rotational symmetry which occurs in a plane pattern is the rotational symmetry of the plane lattice

is quite general, being equally applicable to three-dimensional patterns and so may be extended to CONCEPT No. 47.

CONCEPT No. 47.   THE HIGHEST ROTATIONAL SYMMETRY WHICH OCCURS IN A CRYSTAL IS THE ROTATIONAL SYMMETRY OF THE SPACE LATTICE OF THAT CRYSTAL.

The influence of the motif on the symmetry of a crystal will be considered further in Chapter 15 at which stage the ideas of the crystalline state will have been developed sufficiently to make a detailed examination of the classification of crystals into various distinctive groups according to rotational symmetry.

In addition to rotational symmetry, space lattices may also be symmetrical about a plane which divides the lattice into mirror-imaged parts.

78

DEFINITION No. 12. A mirror plane of symmetry is any plane which divides a body into halves that are mirror images of one another across the plane.

The more highly symmetrical the lattice the greater the number of mirror planes it contains but whether these are mirror planes in the crystal depends on the shape of the motif, as was seen in CONCEPT No. 23.

CONCEPT No. 23.   Depending on the shape of the motif, the number of mirror planes in a plane pattern may be less than the number in the lattice of the pattern.

Hence CONCEPT No. 48 follows.

CONCEPT No. 48.   DEPENDING ON THE SHAPE OF THE MOTIF, THE NUMBER OF MIRROR PLANES IN A CRYSTAL MAY BE LESS THAN THE NUMBER IN THE SPACE LATTICE OF THE CRYSTAL.

A space lattice also may have a centre of symmetry.

DEFINITION No. 13. A body has a centre of symmetry if for every point in it there is an identical point equidistant from the centre but on the opposite side.

Thus, every lattice point of a space lattice, being indistinguishable from every other point, must be a centre of symmetry. Similarly, following

CONCEPT No. 25.   Unit cells of all plane lattices have a centre of symmetry

the site at the geometrical centre of every one of the infinity of different unit cells that can represent a space lattice also must be a centre of symmetry, for it is through both these sites and the lattice points that a space lattice can be inverted.

CONCEPT No. 24.   A body is inverted through a centre of symmetry by projecting every point of it to a new location exactly the same distance from the centre but on the opposite side.

Clearly, a space lattice, being infinite in extent, has an infinite number of centres of symmetry and, as has just been asserted, every possible unit cell of the lattice necessarily has a centre.

CONCEPT No. 49.   ALL UNIT CELLS OF A SPACE LATTICE HAVE A CENTRE OF SYMMETRY.

Whether the three-dimensional array of atoms in a crystal is symmetrical with respect to a centre depends upon the way in which the atoms occur in the motif, just as is the case for plane patterns.

CONCEPT No. 26.   Whether a unit cell of a plane pattern has a centre of symmetry depends on the shape of the motif.

Extending this concept to three-dimensional crystals, leads to CONCEPT No. 50.

CONCEPT No. 50.   WHETHER THE UNIT CELL OF A CRYSTAL HAS A CENTRE OF SYMMETRY DEPENDS ON THE WAY IN WHICH THE ATOMS OCCUR IN THE MOTIF.

The symmetry operations that have been considered so far — rotation, reflection, and inversion — are demonstrably just as appropriate to the three-dimensional space lattice and pattern of a crystal as to the two-dimensional lattice and pattern for which they were developed in Chapter 4. However, there is an additional operation which can occur in a three-dimensional structure, but which has no two-dimensional counterpart.

This new operation is called ROTARY INVERSION and is derived from the combination of rotation and inversion.

DEFINITION No. 29. A BODY HAS A ROTARY INVERSION AXIS IF IT CAN BE TRANSFORMED TO SELF COINCIDENCE BY THE COMBINED EFFECT OF ROTATION AND INVERSION.

Examine the array of points ABCD shown in Figure 46. This array could represent part of a space lattice or part of a three-dimensional pattern if the points have substance. The array of four points can be transformed to self coincidence by the operation shown in detail for the point A. If this point is subjected to a 90° rotation about the axis xy it is moved to the position A'. The other three points move in an equivalent way. Following the rotation, inversion of the point A' through the centre 1̄ moves it to the position B which is the initial position of one of the other points in the array, specifically the point B. Thus the combined effect of the 90° rotation and the inversion is to move the point A to the location B. The complete set of transfers by the combined operations is:

$$A \rightarrow A' \rightarrow B$$
$$B \rightarrow B' \rightarrow C$$
$$C \rightarrow C' \rightarrow D$$
$$D \rightarrow D' \rightarrow A$$

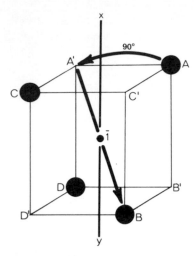

Figure 46. Diagram showing the operation of a 4-fold rotary inversion axis

It is instructive to follow carefully these movements so that the combined effect of the two operations is fully appreciated. Since the final set of locations of the points is identical with the initial set, the two sets are self coincident and the operation of rotation plus inversion is, by DEFINITION No. 8, a symmetry operation. This operation is called a rotary inversion, specifically a 4-fold rotary inversion and is designated $\bar{4}$ (bar four).

It is very important to realize that the axis xy is not necessarily a 4-fold rotation axis of symmetry even though rotation through 90° about it is an integral part of the 4-fold rotary inversion element. However, in deriving the complete set of rotary inversion elements it is convenient to regard each of them simply as the combination of an N-fold rotation axis and a centre. Thus the complete set of combinations is:

$$1 + \bar{1} \rightarrow \bar{1}$$
$$2 + \bar{1} \rightarrow \bar{2}$$
$$3 + \bar{1} \rightarrow \bar{3}$$
$$4 + \bar{1} \rightarrow \bar{4}$$
$$6 + \bar{1} \rightarrow \bar{6}$$

Each of these five symmetry elements is a line (an axis) which passes through the centre ($\bar{1}$) with which it is combined to form the rotary inversion axis (or rotary invertor) as defined in DEFINITION No. 29.

With respect to the five rotary invertors it is necessary to note the following.

(i) The $\bar{1}$ rotary invertor is obviously identical with a centre of symmetry and is not a different symmetry element.

(ii) The $\bar{2}$ rotary invertor is not a different symmetry element either, for as shown

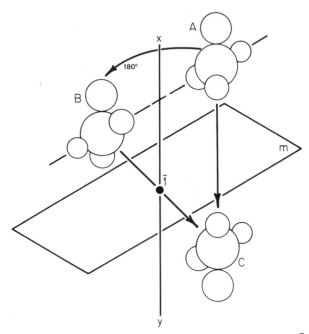

Figure 47. Diagram showing the equivalence of a $\bar{2}$ rotary inversion axis and a mirror plane of symmetry. Rotation through $180°$ about the axis xy transforms the group of atoms at A to the group at B which is inverted through the centre $\bar{1}$ to C. This group is also produced identically by simple mirror reflection of the group at A across the plane m

in Figure 47 it is exactly equivalent to mirror reflection across a plane passing through the centre at right angles to the axis.

(iii) The $\bar{3}$ is truly identical to the combination of a 3-fold rotation axis and a centre but for convenience it is usually considered to be a distinct element

with the symbol ▲ .

(iv) The $\bar{4}$ is irreducible, as shown in Figure 46, and therefore is a distinct and

different element with the symbol ◩ .

(v) The $\bar{6}$ is exactly equivalent to the combination of a 3-fold rotation axis and mirror reflection across a plane at right angles to the axis, but for convenience

it is usually considered to be a distinct element with the symbol ⬡ .

Thus, only the $\bar{3}$, $\bar{4}$, and $\bar{6}$ are accepted as symmetry elements additional to those which have been previously identified and so the complete set of symmetry elements that may occur in space lattices is:

the rotation axes	$1, 2, 3, 4, 6$
the centre of symmetry	$\bar{1}$
the rotary inversion axes	$\bar{3}, \bar{4}, \bar{6}$, and
the mirror plane	m

remembering from

DEFINITION No. 14. A symmetry element is any point, line or plane in a body about which an appropriate symmetry operation will transform the body to self coincidence.

The complete set of ten elements was known in fact to crystallographers long before it was suspected that the internal structure of crystals consists of regular arrays of atoms. The existence of the elements was deduced from studies of the external shapes of mineral crystals found occurring naturally and which are now known to be a consequence of the internal order. In this early work the symmetry of the external shape was described by the collection of appropriate symmetry elements that specified the shape features visible to the unaided eye. For this reason the elements are called the MACROSCOPIC SYMMETRY ELEMENTS.

DEFINITION No. 30. THE MACROSCOPIC SYMMETRY ELEMENTS ARE THOSE SYMMETRY ELEMENTS WHICH MAY INFLUENCE THE EXTERNAL SHAPE OF A FREELY FORMED CRYSTAL IN SUCH A WAY AS TO BE DETECTABLE WITH THE UNAIDED EYE AND CONSIST OF ROTATION $(1, 2, 3, 4, 6)$, REFLECTION (m), INVERSION $(\bar{1})$, AND ROTARY INVERSION $(\bar{3}, \bar{4}, \bar{6})$.

It will be seen in Chapter 16 that there are other symmetry elements which have no influence on external shape at all but only concern the structure at an atomic level. These elements are the microscopic symmetry elements but do not concern this stage of development of the ideas of crystallography.

Chapter 11

Point Groups

In considering the external symmetry of any freely formed crystal, every macroscopic symmetry element necessarily acts upon or passes through the point at the geometrical centre of the crystal. A rotation axis or rotary inversion axis must pass through this point otherwise rotation about the axis could not produce a self coincident condition of the crystal, a mirror plane divides the crystal into halves and therefore must pass through the point, and of course a centre of symmetry must be located exactly at the centre of the crystal.

Thus the total macroscopic symmetry of a crystal is that collection of symmetry elements which is associated with the point at the centre of the crystal.

Turning now to examine the total symmetry of the array of points constituting the space lattice of any crystal, exactly the same considerations apply. Since every point of a space lattice is, by DEFINITION No. 24, indistinguishable from every other point, the collection of elements defining the symmetry of the lattice must be associated with each and every point of the lattice. For example, if the crystal has rotational symmetry then the appropriate rotation axis in the correct orientation must pass through the lattice point at the geometrical centre of the crystal and, since this point is not distinguishable, the same kind of rotation axis in the same orientation must pass through every other of the infinity of lattice points in the space lattice of that crystal. Thus to completely specify the macroscopic symmetry of the lattice it is necessary only to specify the symmetry at any point in that lattice. The collection of symmetry elements at any point of the lattice is termed the POINT SYMMETRY, the POINT GROUP OF SYMMETRY or sometimes the CRYSTAL CLASS.

DEFINITION No. 31. THE POINT GROUP OF SYMMETRY OF A CRYSTAL IS
THAT COLLECTION OF MACROSCOPIC SYMMETRY
ELEMENTS WHICH OCCURS AT EVERY LATTICE
POINT OF THE SPACE LATTICE OF THE CRYSTAL.

Of course, the point symmetry of the lattice of a crystal may be different from the point symmetry of the crystal itself as a consequence of the shape of the motif, see CONCEPT Nos. 47, 48, and 50.

The question now arises: what are the possible combinations of the ten macroscopic symmetry elements that determine how many kinds of point symmetry exist? It has been seen already in Chapter 4 that four mirror planes and a

4-fold rotation axis are compatible with one another (Figure 29(c)), while the combinations of 3-fold and 4-fold axes, or 4-fold and 6-fold axes are not, at least in plane lattices.

A detailed analysis of the compatibility of the ten elements in all possible combinations to answer this question is far beyond the scope of this book but has been well detailed in many excellent but more advanced works. In particular the analysis given in the section on crystallography in *Encyclopaedia Britannica* is worthwhile reading.

The analysis of the problem shows that, from the very large number of possible groupings of the symmetry elements, only 32 are compatible combinations of one or more of them. Thus, there exist only 32 point groups of symmetry.

At one time or another these 32 groups have been identified by several different notations of which the most widely accepted is probably that known as the Hermann–Mauguin notation and this is the system that will be used here. In the following description of the 32 point groups of symmetry the full Hermann–Mauguin symbol is given together with the accepted abbreviation in parentheses.

SET A

1	(1)	a 1-fold rotation axis, that is, no symmetry at all.
$\bar{1}$	$(\bar{1})$	a centre of symmetry and nothing else.

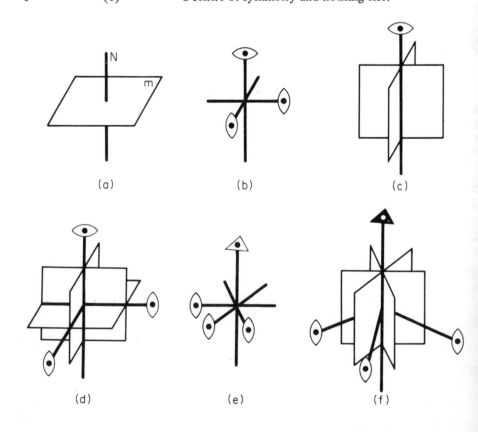

(a)   (b)   (c)

(d)   (e)   (f)

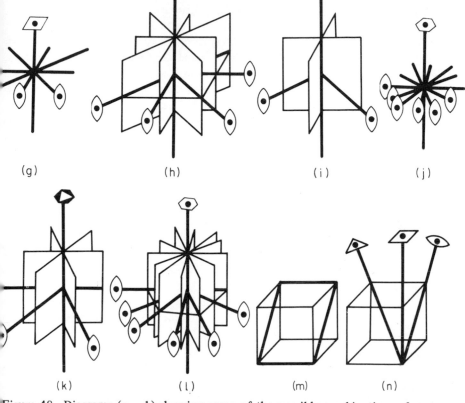

(g) (h) (i) (j)

(k) (l) (m) (n)

Figure 48. Diagrams (a — 1) showing some of the possible combinations of macroscopic symmetry elements in point groups, together with (m) and (n) showing, respectively, a diagonal mirror plane, and the locations of 2-fold, 3-fold, and 4-fold axes in a cube

SET B

2	(2)	a lone 2-fold rotation axis.
m	(m)	a single mirror plane.
2/m	(2/m)	a 2-fold rotation axis with a mirror plane at right angles to it (see Figure 48(a) for N = 2).

SET C

222	(222)	three 2-fold rotation axes at right angles to one another (see Figure 48(b)).
2mm	(mm)	two mirror planes at right angles to one another with a 2-fold rotation axis along the line of intersection of the planes (see Figure 48(c)).
2/m 2/m 2/m	(mmm)	three mirror planes at right angles to one another with a 2-fold rotation axis along each of the three lines of intersection (see Figure 48(d)).

SET D

3	(3)	a lone 3-fold rotation axis.
$\bar{3}$	($\bar{3}$)	a lone $\bar{3}$-rotary inversion axis.
3m	(3m)	three mirror planes at $120°$ to one another intersecting along a 3-fold axis (similar to Figure 48(c)).
32	(32)	a 3-fold rotation axis passing at right angles through the intersection of three 2-fold axes at $120°$ to each other (see Figure 48(e)).
$\bar{3}$ 2/m	($\bar{3}$m)	three mirror planes at $120°$ to each other intersecting along a $\bar{3}$-rotary invertor with three 2-fold axes at right angles to the $\bar{3}$ and midway between the mirror planes (see Figure 48(f)).

SET E

4	(4)	a lone 4-fold rotation axis.
$\bar{4}$	($\bar{4}$)	a lone $\bar{4}$-rotary invertor.
4/m	(4/m)	a 4-fold rotation axis with a mirror plane at right angles to it (see Figure 48(a) for N = 4).
422	(42)	a 4-fold rotation axis passing at right angles through the intersection of four 2-fold rotation axes at $45°$ to one another (see Figure 48(g)).
4mm	(4mm)	four mirror planes at $45°$ to one another with a 4-fold rotation axis along the line of intersection (similar to Figure 48(c)).
4/m 2/m 2/m	(4/mmm)	four mirror planes at $45°$ to one another intersecting along a 4-fold rotation axis; an additional mirror plane at right angles to the 4-fold axis intersects the other mirror planes along four 2-fold rotation axes (see Figure 48(h)).
$\bar{4}$2m	($\bar{4}$2m)	two mirror planes intersecting along a $\bar{4}$-rotary invertor with two 2-fold rotation axes at right angles to the $\bar{4}$ and midway between the mirror planes (see Figure 48(i)).

SET F

6	(6)	a lone 6-fold rotation axis.
$\bar{6}$	($\bar{6}$)	a lone $\bar{6}$-rotary invertor.
6/m	(6/m)	a 6-fold rotation axis with a mirror plane at right angles to it (see Figure 48(a) for N = 6).
6mm	(6mm)	six mirror planes at $30°$ to one another intersecting along a 6-fold rotation axis (similar to Figure 48(c)).
622	($\bar{6}$2)	a 6-fold rotation axis passing at right angles through the intersection of six 2-fold rotation axes at $30°$ to one another (see Figure 48(j)).

$\bar{6}2m$	$(\bar{6}2m)$	three mirror planes at 60° to each other intersecting along a $\bar{6}$-rotary invertor, each mirror plane containing a 2-fold rotation axis at right angles to the $\bar{6}$ (see Figure 48(k)).
$6/m\ 2/m\ 2/m$	$(6/mmm)$	six mirror planes at 30° to each other intersecting along a 6-fold rotation axis, each mirror plane containing a 2-fold rotation axis at right angles to the 6-fold axis, and lying in a mirror plane also at right angles to the 6-fold axis (see Figure 48(l)).

SET G

23	(23)	three 2-fold axes at right angles to one another and parallel to the edges of a cube with four 3-fold axes parallel to the body diagonals, i.e. four 3-fold axes at 70°32′ to one another.
$2/m\ \bar{3}$	$(m3)$	three mirror planes, parallel to the faces of a cube, intersecting along three 2-fold axes parallel to the edges of the cube with four $\bar{3}$-rotary invertors parallel to the body diagonals of the cube.
$\bar{4}3m$	$(\bar{4}3m)$	three $\bar{4}$-rotary invertors parallel to the edges of a cube, with four 3-fold rotation axes parallel to the body diagonals and six mirror planes, each containing a face diagonal (see Figure 48(m) for one such mirror plane).
432	(43)	three 4-fold rotation axes parallel to the edges of a cube with four 3-fold rotation axes parallel to the body diagonals and six 2-fold rotation axes parallel to the face diagonals (see Figure 48(n) for examples of the 2-fold, 3-fold, and 4-fold rotation axes).
$4/m\ \bar{3}\ 2/m$	$(m3m)$	three 4-fold rotation axes parallel to the edges of a cube with four $\bar{3}$-rotary invertors parallel to the body diagonals, six 2-fold rotation axes parallel to the face diagonals, and nine mirror planes, three of which are parallel to the faces and the other six containing a face diagonal as shown in Figure 48(m). This group is the most highly symmetrical of all the point groups of symmetry.

These 32 combinations are the only possible ways in which the 1, 2, 3, 4, 6, $\bar{1}$, $\bar{3}$, $\bar{4}$, $\bar{6}$, and m symmetry elements can combine together and although a thorough understanding of the significance of the 32 combinations is rather beyond the scope of the concepts in this book it is important to realize that every crystal must have macroscopic symmetry that can be described by one of the 32 combinations for there are no others. Thus crystals could be classified according to macroscopic symmetry, but they are not for there exists a better means of classification.

Chapter 12

Crystal Systems

In the detailed description of the 32 point groups of symmetry in Chapter 11 a most important feature of the 32 combinations was emphasized by the way in which the groups were distributed among the seven sets A, B, C, D, E, F, and G.

Careful examination of each of these seven sets reveals that the member groups have a common symmetry component. Look for them.

SET A: 1, $\bar{1}$.
The common feature is a 1-fold axis (remember that a $\bar{1}$ can be regarded as the combination of a 1-fold rotation axis and a centre).

SET B: 2, m, 2/m.
The common feature is a 2-fold axis (remember that a mirror plane m is equivalent to a $\bar{2}$-rotary invertor which in turn can be regarded as a 2-fold rotation axis and a centre).

SET C: 222, 2 mm, 2/m2/m2/m.
The common feature is three 2-fold rotation axes at right angles to one another.

SET D: 3, $\bar{3}$, 3 m, 32, $\bar{3}$ 2/m.
The common feature is a 3-fold axis.

SET E: 4, $\bar{4}$, 4/m, 422, 4 mm, 4/m2/m2/m, $\bar{4}$2 m.
The common feature is a 4-fold axis.

SET F: 6, $\bar{6}$, 6/m, 6 mm, 622, $\bar{6}$2 m, 6/m 2/m 2/m.
The common feature is a 6-fold axis.

SET G: 23, 2/m $\bar{3}$, $\bar{4}$3 m, 432, 4/m $\bar{3}$ 2/m.
The common feature is four 3-fold axes at $70°32'$ to one another, i.e. parallel to the body diagonals of a cube; note that the symbol for the common feature is the second term in the group.

Thus, there is a logical basis for the distribution of the point groups of symmetry among the seven sets. Since all crystals have macroscopic symmetry that necessarily must be specified by one of the 32 point groups, it follows that it must be possible o classify all crystals into these seven sets according to the dominant feature of otational symmetry.

The sets are called CRYSTAL SYSTEMS and each one of them has a listinguishing name.

Set	Essential symmetry	Name
A	Only 1-fold axes, i.e. no rotational symmetry at all	TRICLINIC
B	One 2-fold axis	MONOCLINIC
C	Three mutually perpendicular 2-fold axes	ORTHORHOMBIC
D	One 3-fold axis	RHOMBOHEDRAL (also termed TRIGONAL)
E	One 4-fold axis	TETRAGONAL
F	One 6-fold axis	HEXAGONAL
G	Four 3-fold axes at $70°32'$ to each other	CUBIC

DEFINITION No. 32. A CRYSTAL SYSTEM IS ONE OF THE SEVEN BASIC CATEGORIES, DETERMINED BY ESSENTIAL ROTATIONAL SYMMETRY PROPERTIES, INTO WHICH ALL CRYSTALS MAY BE CLASSIFIED; THE SEVEN SYSTEMS ARE: TRICLINIC, MONOCLINIC, ORTHORHOMBIC, RHOMBOHEDRAL (TRIGONAL), TETRAGONAL, HEXAGONAL, AND CUBIC.

When applied to the space lattices of crystals, the classification into seven systems has certain ramifications concerning the shape of the unit cell that best and most simply displays the macroscopic symmetry of the lattices. It will be remembered that the unit cell of a space lattice is a parallelepiped with lattice parameters a, b, c, α, β, and γ (CONCEPT No. 44). The relative values of these parameters required by the minimum symmetry properties of each crystal system are as follows.

TRICLINIC $\qquad a \neq b \neq c. \ \alpha \neq \beta \neq \gamma$

The three unit translations have any lengths and are at any angles to one another as a consequence of the absence of rotational symmetry in the system, i.e. the presence of only 1-fold rotation axes.

MONOCLINIC $\qquad a \neq b \neq c, \ \alpha = \gamma = 90° \neq \beta$

The three unit translations have any lengths; two pairs of them (a and b, b and c) are at right angles to one another, the other pair (a and c) are at any angle (β). By convention, the 2-fold axis which characterizes this system is parallel to the **b** translation of the unit cell.

ORTHORHOMBIC $a \neq b \neq c, \alpha = \beta = \gamma = 90°$
The three unit translations have any lengths but are at right angles to one another. The three 2-fold axes of the system are parallel to the three edges of the unit cell, i.e. to the three unit translations.

RHOMBOHEDRAL $a = b = c, \alpha = \beta = \gamma \neq 90°$
The three unit translations have the same length and are equally inclined to one another but not at right angles. The 3-fold axis of the system is parallel to that body diagonal which for $\alpha > 90°$ is shorter than the others and for $\alpha < 90°$ is longer than the others as shown in Figure 49.

TETRAGONAL $a = b \neq c, \alpha = \beta = \gamma = 90°$
Two of the unit translations have the same length, different from the third, which by convention is the translation c, and all are at right angles to one another. The 4-fold axis of the system is parallel to the c translation.

HEXAGONAL $a = b \neq c, \alpha = \beta = 90°, \gamma = 120°$
Two of the three unit translations, **a** and **b**, have the same length and are inclined at 120° to each other. The third unequal translation, by convention the c translation, is at right angles to the other two. The 6-fold axis of the system is parallel to the c translation.

CUBIC $a = b = c, \alpha = \beta = \gamma = 90°$
The three unit translations have the same length and are at right angles to one another. The four 3-fold axes of the system are parallel to the body diagonals of the cube, i.e. at an angle of 54°44′ to the edges and at 70°32′ to each other.

These seven unit cells represent the total number of different ways in which it is possible to draw a parallelepiped. However, it should be clearly understood that in the specifications of the shapes of the unit cells the sign $\neq$ does not have the meaning generally ascribed to it in mathematics, but means USUALLY not equal to by reason of symmetry, and accidental equality may occur. The implications of this rather specialized meaning will be examined in Chapter 14.

An examination of the unit cells of the seven crystal systems may now be made in a similar way to the examination of the unit cells of the five plane lattices in Chapter 3. It will be remembered that the properties of these cells were explored by

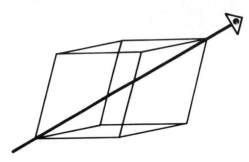

Figure 49. Diagram showing the 3-fold rotation axis in a rhombohedral unit cell having $\alpha < 90°$

eeking the answers to three questions about them and it is convenient to adopt the ame procedure to explore the unit cells of space lattices by posing three similar uestions.

Chapter 13

The Unit Cell of a Crystal

The first question concerning the unit cell of a crystal is: how many fundamentally different shapes of unit cell are there?

It has been seen in Chapter 12 that there are seven crystal systems each having a distinctive cell (parallelepiped), but are these seven cells fundamentally different and if so do they comprise the complete set of fundamentally different cells? The answer to both questions is 'yes'.

Consider for example the cubic unit cell. It should be realized that all such cells necessarily have identical minimum symmetry of four 3-fold axes at $70°32'$ to each other, i.e. along the body diagonals of the cell, regardless of the actual lengths of the sides $a = b = c$. Any parallelepiped having such four 3-fold axes is necessarily a cube and a crystal with that parallelepiped as unit cell is cubic. A crystal which does not have the four 3-fold axes cannot be classified in the cubic system and, in general, the unit cell will not be a cube. Thus, all crystals of the cubic system have the common feature of four 3-fold axes at $70°32'$ to one another and the unit cell of the crystals are identical in this distinguishing respect regardless of the value of $a = b = c$.

Similarly all crystals of the tetragonal system have one 4-fold axis and the unit cell is necessarily a right prism with $a = b \neq c$. The precise values of $a = b$ and of c are not important, and further, it is inconsequential whether c is larger or smaller than $a = b$. All that is required for a crystal to be tetragonal is the essential 4-fold axis and all crystals which have this minimum symmetry property have basically identical unit cells.

The same argument can be applied to the other five crystal systems. All crystals having one 6-fold axis are hexagonal with basically the same unit cell regardless of the actual values of $a = b$ and c, but of course to have the 6-fold axis the angle between a and b must be $120°$ and the other angles α and β must be $90°$.

All crystals with one 3-fold axis are rhombohedral and the unit cells are basically the same regardless of the actual values of the translations $a = b = c$ and of the angle α. All crystals with one 2-fold axis are monoclinic and the unit cells are basically identical for all $a \neq b \neq c$ and β. All crystals with no symmetry (except perhaps for a centre) are triclinic and the general unit cells are basically the same. Finally, all crystals with three 2-fold axes at right angles to one another are orthorhombic and the unit cells, necessarily right rectangular prisms, are basically identical for all $a \neq b \neq c$.

The essential feature which determines the system for any crystal is quite clearly he rotational symmetry of that crystal. It is highly probable (although by no means necessary) that the symmetry of a crystal influences the values of a, b, c, α, β, and γ in such a way that the shape of the cell is also distinguishing, but this is a less fundamental property in classification. Nevertheless, the shape of the unit cell and the size of it have great importance to crystal structure as they specify the distribution in space of the lattice points at which are located the motifs of the structure.

To summarize then, the classification of crystals into the seven systems according to rotational symmetry means that there are seven fundamentally different unit cells which, in most cases, can be used also for purposes of classification.

The second question concerns the number of lattice points associated with the unit cell. This is certainly a most important aspect of structure for, as there is one motif at each point, the total number of motifs in the unit cell must be the same as the number of points in the cell.

To find this number refer to Figure 50 to see that there are three different kinds of site in the unit cell at which lattice points may occur. These are the sites B, F, and C at which grossly exaggerated points have been drawn. It should be evident that additional points cannot be present on the edges of the cell for each edge must be one unit translation as required by DEFINITION No. 28.

First examine the body site B which is located totally within the boundaries of the cell. A lattice point at such a site must be associated wholly with the cell as it is not shared with any other. If the cell contains a number b of these body points then the contribution of them must be $1 \times b$ to the total number n of points in the cell.

Points at the other kinds of sites F and C lie on the surface of the cell and are shared with other adjacent cells so that only a part of any such point is associated with any particular cell. To determine this part it is necessary to examine each kind of site and find the number of cells with which it is associated. In doing this it is noted first that two adjacent cells contact over a face so that a FACE point such as that at site F contributes only 1/2 of a point to each cell. Thus, if there is a number f of such points the total contribution of them to the total number n of points in the cell is $1/2 \times f$. Secondly, it is noted that eight cells contact at each

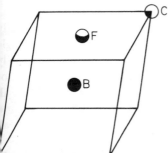

Figure 50. Diagram showing (exaggerated) body (B), face (F), and corner (C) points in a unit cell

corner so that a CORNER point such as that located at the site C contributes, on average, only 1/8 of a point to the cell. Since such a point as C is necessarily located at each of the eight corners of the unit cell the total contribution of them to n is $1/8 \times 8 = 1$. The corner points contribute one whole point to the unit cell.

Summing these contributions the total number n of lattice points in a unit cell is

$$n = 1 + (\tfrac{1}{2} \times f) + b$$

For $b = f = 0$ the unit cell has points located only at the corners and there is one such point associated with each cell, which by DEFINITION No. 6 is a PRIMITIVE UNIT CELL.

DEFINITION No. 6. A primitive unit cell contains a single lattice point.

The symbol that is used to signify that a unit cell is primitive is the letter P.

Alternatively, a unit cell is not primitive if one or both of b or f is not zero for under these circumstances, the cell contains more than one lattice point, i.e. from DEFINITION No. 7.

DEFINITION No. 7. A non-primitive unit cell contains two or more lattice points.

It is important to note that there are certain limitations on the values that the numbers n, f, and b can have.

(a) A unit cell may contain any number of lattice points within the boundaries so that the number b may be any integer.

(b) Since all unit cells derived from the same three unit translations must be identical, the face points must occur in pairs so that the number f must be even and consequently $(\tfrac{1}{2} \times f)$ is an integer. This requirement is shown in Figure 51 — for every face point F there must be a corresponding face point F otherwise the top and bottom faces of the unit cell would be different and so two parallel planes in the space lattice would contain different arrangements of points contrary to the DEFINITION No. 24 of a space lattice.

(c) Following (a) and (b) the number n of lattice points in any unit cell must be an integer, $n = 1 + (\tfrac{1}{2} \times f) + b$, and a simple relationship exists between the value of n and the volume of the infinite number of different unit cells that occur in any space lattice.

CONCEPT No. 11 specifies that there is an infinite number of different unit cells for any space lattice and, of these, an infinite number are primitive, and an infinite

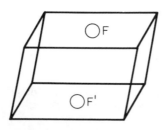

Figure 51. Diagram showing that the existence of a face point F requires an equivalent point F' in the opposite face

number are non-primitive. Consider for a moment just one of the infinity of different primitive unit cells. By DEFINITION No. 6 the cell contains a single lattice point as does every one of the other identical cells with the same unit translations. The volume of the cell must be the volume of space associated with one lattice point, that is, the volume for one lattice point. This volume is determined solely by the way in which the points occur in the space lattice and obviously is not dependent in any way on the selection of a particular unit cell in preference to any of the others.

This same concept arose in Chapter 3 in consideration of plane lattices.

CONCEPT No. 14.   For any particular plane lattice, the infinite number of
different primitive unit cells which can be used to represent
it all have exactly the same area, the area A per lattice point.

This concept can now be extended to the three-dimensional case.

CONCEPT No. 51.   FOR ANY PARTICULAR SPACE LATTICE, THE
INFINITE NUMBER OF DIFFERENT PRIMITIVE UNIT
CELLS WHICH CAN BE USED TO REPRESENT IT ALL
HAVE EXACTLY THE SAME VOLUME, THE VOLUME V
PER LATTICE POINT.

Now, non-primitive cells contain an integral number of lattice points necessarily more than one, and so the volume of such a cell must be the volume associated with that integral number of points. If the volume associated with one point is V then clearly the volume of a primitive cell is also V. It follows that the volume of a non-primitive cell containing n points is simply $n \times V$. Thus

CONCEPT No. 15.   The area of any unit cell in a plane lattice is the product of n
and A, where n is the number of lattice points in the unit cell
and A is the area of a primitive unit cell of that lattice

can be extended to the three-dimensional case of a space lattice.

CONCEPT No. 52.   THE VOLUME OF ANY UNIT CELL IN A SPACE
LATTICE IS THE PRODUCT OF n AND V, WHERE n IS
THE NUMBER OF LATTICE POINTS IN THE UNIT CELL
AND V IS THE VOLUME OF A PRIMITIVE UNIT CELL
OF THAT LATTICE.

Of course the actual volume of a unit cell is necessarily determined by the values of the lattice parameters and is given by:

$$\text{volume} = \mathbf{abc}\sqrt{(1 - \cos^2 \alpha - \cos^2 \beta - \cos^2 \gamma + 2 \cos \alpha \cos \beta \cos \gamma)}$$

The final question which needs to be answered is concerned with the reasons for selection of one particular cell in preference to all other possible cells to represent some space lattice. Of all the primitive and non-primitive cells that are available, which one is chosen to represent the lattice and why? Certainly any one of the infinity of possible cells could be used but usually two criteria are adopted in selecting the particular cell to be used. These criteria relate to geometrical simplicity and the need to display the symmetry properties of the lattice. Following

CONCEPT No. 16.   The unit cell which is usually used to represent a plane lattice is that cell which is geometrically the simplest

the equivalent requirement for a space lattice is stated in CONCEPT No. 53.

CONCEPT No. 53.   THE UNIT CELL WHICH IS USED TO REPRESENT A SPACE LATTICE IS A CELL WHICH IS GEOMETRI-CALLY SIMPLE.

However, this criterion oversimplifies the selection, for the cell chosen to represent a space lattice must necessarily be one which adequately displays the symmetry properties of the lattice, so that the crystal system is easily identified. This requirement leads to CONCEPT No. 54.

CONCEPT No. 54.   THE UNIT CELL WHICH BEST REPRESENTS A PARTICULAR SPACE LATTICE IS THAT CELL WHICH, IN ADDITION TO BEING GEOMETRICALLY SIMPLE, CLEARLY IDENTIFIES THE ROTATIONAL SYMMETRY PROPERTIES OF THE LATTICE.

The two criteria taken together result in both primitive and non-primitive cells being used for different space lattices and crystal systems as will be demonstrated in Chapter 14.

Chapter 14

Bravais Lattices

If geometrical simplicity was the only criterion for the selection of a unit cell then the simplest primitive cell for each system would be chosen to represent the crystals of that system. However as the unit cell is also required to show the symmetry of the lattice, particularly the rotational symmetry, and so clearly identify the crystal system, it is necessary to consider the circumstances under which the primitive cell fails to satisfy this requirement.

The necessity for non-primitive unit cells can be appreciated by considering the most general unit cell of all and investigating the consequences of special relationships between the lengths of the cell edges and the angles between them.

The most general unit cell is

TYPE 1: $a \neq b \neq c, \alpha \neq \beta \neq \gamma$

Essential symmetry : nil, other than the possibility of a centre $\bar{1}$.
Crystal system   : triclinic.
Lattice points   : in the simple cells the points occur only at the corners and so the cell is primitive P with $n = 1$.

Of the infinity of possible primitive unit cells that could be used to represent the triclinic space lattice the cell usually selected is the one which is geometrically the simplest and this requires that a, b, and c have the most similar values consistent with the angles α, β, and γ being as close as possible to $90°$.

The other six crystal systems and the unit cells needed to adequately represent the space lattices of those systems will now be found as special cases of the triclinic unit cell.

TYPE 2: $a \neq b \neq c, \alpha = \gamma = 90° \neq \beta$

Essential symmetry : one 2-fold rotation axis parallel to the b translation.
Crystal system   : monoclinic.
Lattice points   : at the cell corners, thus the cell is primitive P with $n = 1$.

As both the angles α and γ are $90°$ a single 2-fold rotation axis is present, with the consequence that the crystal system is monoclinic.

98

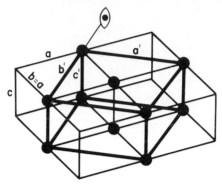

Figure 52. Diagram showing that the space lattice represented by the general unit cell (light lines) with parameters $a = b \neq c$, $\alpha = \beta \neq \gamma$ has a 2-fold axis parallel to one of the C face diagonals and so is better represented by the base centred monoclinic unit cell (heavy lines) with parameters a', b', and c' ($= c$)

TYPE 3: $a = b \neq c, \alpha = \beta \neq \gamma$

Essential symmetry : one 2-fold rotation axis parallel to the diagonal between the a and b unit translations in the C face.

Crystal system : monoclinic, because of the 2-fold axis.

The 2-fold rotation axis is poorly located as a face diagonal in the cell for which $a = b \neq c$, $\alpha = \beta \neq \gamma$. However, by selecting a different set of axes in the space lattice a different unit cell can be identified with $a' \neq b' \neq c'$ (where $c' = c$), and $\alpha' = \gamma' = 90° \neq \beta'$, which is precisely the relationship between parameters usually adopted for the monoclinic system, see Chapter 12. In this new unit cell the 2-fold rotation axis is obvious, having the conventional location parallel to the b translation.

The two unit cells and the relationship between them are shown in Figure 52. It is evident from this diagram that, as a consequence of selecting a unit cell which clearly identifies the essential symmetry of the space lattice and also conforms with the conventional monoclinic cell parameters, the cell is non-primitive. The unit cell with the 2-fold rotation axis parallel to the b' translation has lattice points at each corner and also in the centres of two opposite faces. Thus, following

CONCEPT No. 17. A centred unit cell has lattice points at the corners together with an additional point at the geometrical centre

it is clear that the new unit cell is a centred cell. The faces that are centred are those having the a' and b' unit translations as edges, which by convention is the C face. Thus the unit cell has lattice points in the centres of the C faces and is said to be BASE CENTRED on the C face; the symbol C is used to denote this particular kind of unit cell. Note that in other lattices, or by labelling the edges in a different way, it is possible to define a unit cell with points in the centres of the A faces or the B faces; such cells are termed A and B base centred respectively.

DEFINITION No. 33. A BASE CENTRED UNIT CELL HAS LATTICE POINTS AT THE CELL CORNERS AND, IN ADDITION, AT THE CENTRES OF TWO OPPOSITE FACES.

Lattice points : the base centred monoclinic unit cell shown in Figure 52 has two face centering points so that $f = 2$ and the total number of points in the cell is $n = 1 + (½ \times 2) = 1 + 1 = 2$; there are two lattice points in the C base centred unit cell.

TYPE 4: $a = b = c, \alpha = \beta = \gamma$
Essential symmetry : one 3-fold rotation axis parallel to the unequal body diagonal of the cell.
Crystal system : rhombohedral, because of the 3-fold axis.
Lattice points : the unit cell is primitive and contains one point.
 The equality of the cell edges and of the angles between them generates the 3-fold rotation axis characteristic of the rhombohedral system but the cell of course remains primitive. The essential symmetry of the rhombohedral system is adequately identified as the long body diagonal of the cell for $\alpha < 90°$ (see Figure 49), or the short body diagonal for $\alpha > 90°$, and it is this cell which is always used since no other can identify the location of the 3-fold axis as well.

TYPE 5: $a = b = c, \alpha = \beta = \gamma = 90°$
Essential symmetry : four 3-fold axes at $70°32'$ to each other and at $54°44'$ to the cell edges.
Crystal system : cubic.
Lattice points : the unit cell is primitive P and contains a single lattice point.
 The cell of TYPE 5 and also of TYPES 6 and 7 are special cases of the cell TYPE 4, differing only by the angle between the three equal translations. For the special conditions that the angle α is $90°$ (TYPE 5), $109°28'$ (TYPE 6) or $60°$ (TYPE 7) three additional 3-fold rotation axes are generated and so the unit cell has the essential symmetry of the cubic system and not the lesser symmetry (one 3-fold axis) of the rhombohedral system.

TYPE 6: $a = b = c, \alpha = \beta = \gamma = 109°28'$
Essential symmetry : four 3-fold rotation axes, one parallel to the short body diagonal of the cell and the others parallel to the three cell edges.
Crystal system : cubic, as the four 3-fold rotation axes are at an angle of $70°32'$ to each other and consequently for the precise value of $\alpha = \beta = \gamma = 109°28'$ the space lattice does not have the

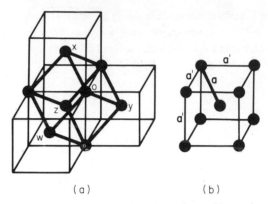

(a)   (b)

Figure 53. Diagrams showing that the space
lattice represented by the primitive unit cell
(heavy lines) having parameters $a = b = c$ and
$\alpha = 109° 28'$ has 3-fold rotation axes parallel to
the cell edges and the short body diagonal and
so is better represented by a body centred cubic
unit cell (light lines) with parameter $a' = 2a/\sqrt{3}$

essential symmetry of the rhombohedral system, but rather,
the higher symmetry requirement of the cubic system.

The unit cell with $a = b = c$, $\alpha = \beta = \gamma = 109°32'$ is shown by heavy lines in
Figure 53. In this cell the four 3-fold rotation axes are reasonably well defined as
the cell edges ow, ox, oy and the short body diagonal oz, but the shape of the cell
does not clearly identify the cubic system. A better unit cell for the space lattice is
shown by light lines and in Figure 53(b). This new cell is a cube (having parameter
a') with the 3-fold axes parallel to the body diagonals and is obviously
non-primitive.

Lattice points   : the cell has points at the corners as well as an additional
                         point at the geometrical centre, that is, $b = 1$ and so the total
                         number of lattice points in the cell is $n = 1 + (1 \times 1) = 1 + 1 = 2$.

The non-primitive cubic unit cell contains two lattice points and since one of
these is located at the geometrical centre of the cell it is called a BODY CENTRED
CELL.

DEFINITION No. 34. A BODY CENTRED UNIT CELL HAS LATTICE POINTS
                    AT EACH CORNER AND AN ADDITIONAL POINT AT
                    THE GEOMETRICAL CENTRE.

The symbol that is used to denote this kind of unit cell is I, being derived from
the word 'inner-centred' or from the German 'innenzentriert' meaning body (or
inner) centred. Note that the symbol B cannot be used for a body centred cell since
this is the symbol that is used to denote a cell base centred on the B faces.

Since the body centred cubic (abbreviation: BCC) unit cell contains two lattice points it must have exactly twice the volume of the primitive cell shown by the heavy lines in Figure 53(a). The simple relationship between the volumes of the two different unit cells indicates that there should also be a simple relationship between the lengths of the edges of them. As the edge length (unit translation) of the primitive cell is a and of the body centred cell is a', then the edge of the primitive cell $a = \sqrt{3}a'/2$, which is half the body diagonal of the body centred unit cell, Figure 53(b).

TYPE 7: $a = b = c, \alpha = \beta = \gamma = 60°$

Essential symmetry : four 3-fold rotation axes, one parallel to the long body diagonal xy (Figure 54) of the cell with the other three passing through the cell; the axes are all at $70°32'$ to each other.

Crystal system : the crystal system is cubic as required by the existence of the four 3-fold axes.

The special value of the angle between the cell edges (60°) generates three additional 3-fold rotation axes, the positions of which are far from obvious in the primitive unit cell. This cell is shown by heavy lines in Figure 54(a) together with an alternative unit cell shown by light lines which, being a cube, clearly locates the 3-fold rotation axes as the four body diagonals. The new unit cell has three equal parameters a' and, as shown in Figure 54(b), it is nonprimitive.

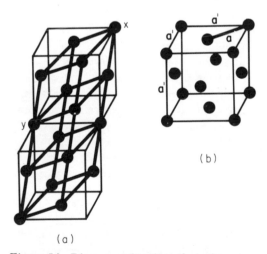

(a)

(b)

Figure 54. Diagrams showing that the space lattice represented by the primitive unit cell (heavy lines) having parameters $a = b = c$ and $\alpha = 60°$ has three 3-fold axes through the cell with another parallel to the long body diagonal and so is better represented by a face centred cubic unit cell (light lines) with parameter $a' = \sqrt{2} a$

Lattice points   : in addition to the lattice points at the corners of the cell there are points in the centres of each of the six faces, thus there are six face points and $f = 6$, so that the total number of points in the cell is $n = 1 + (\frac{1}{2} \times 6) = 1 + 3 = 4$.

The unit cell has four points within it and since it is centred on each of the six faces it is called a FACE CENTRED UNIT CELL.

DEFINITION No. 35. A FACE CENTRED UNIT CELL HAS LATTICE POINTS AT EACH CORNER AND ADDITIONAL POINTS AT THE GEOMETRICAL CENTRE OF EACH OF THE SIX FACES.

The symbol used to denote this kind of cell is F meaning face centred.

Since the face centred cubic unit cell shown in Figure 54(b) contains four lattice points it must have a volume equal, to four-times that of the primitive unit cell shown in Figure 54(a). It follows also that there must be a relationship between the lengths of the unit translations for the two cells. As the edge length of the face centred cubic (abbreviation: FCC) cell is a' and of the primitive cell is a then, $a = a'/\sqrt{2}$, which is one-half the length of the face diagonal of the face centred unit cell, Figure 54(b).

It has now been demonstrated that there are three ways in which it is possible for points, additional to those at the corners, to be present in the unit cell of a space lattice while maintaining the principle that the cell be as simple as possible. These three different kinds of non-primitive unit cells are required to clearly identify the location in the lattice of the essential rotational symmetry which determines the crystal system. The non-primitive cells are the A, B, or C base centred cell, having an additional point at the centre of two opposite faces, the F face centred cell having additional points at the centres of each of the six faces and the I body centred cell having an additional point at the geometrical centre of the cell. These three alternatives represent the only ways in which points, other than the corner points, may be present in a geometrically simple non-primitive cell. An exhaustive study of the consequences of all possible special cases of the general unit cell with $a \neq b \neq c$, $\alpha \neq \beta \neq \gamma$ shows that to represent all the space lattices so produced, with the essential symmetry properties clearly located, requires only primitive P, base centred A, B or C, body centred I, and face centred F unit cells.

CONCEPT No. 55. FOR ANY SPACE LATTICE, THE UNIT CELL WHICH IS GEOMETRICALLY SIMPLE AND WHICH ADEQUATELY DISPLAYS THE ESSENTIAL SYMMETRY OF THE LATTICE MAY BE PRIMITIVE, BASE CENTRED, FACE CENTRED OR BODY CENTRED.

The number of lattice points in each kind of cell has been calculated:

  a primitive unit cell P has   : 1 lattice point;
  a base centred unit cell A, B or C has : 2 lattice points;
  a face centred unit cell F has   : 4 lattice points;
  a body centred unit cell I has   : 2 lattice points;

and since there is one motif at each point, the four kinds of cell must contain a specific number of motifs:

P   : 1 motif;
A, B or C   : 2 motifs;
F   : 4 motifs;
I   : 2 motifs.

So far seven different unit cells and therefore seven different space lattices have been discovered:

triclinic   : P;
monoclinic   : P and C;
rhombohedral   : P;
cubic   : P, I, and F.

There are seven other unit cells (and space lattices too, of course), and these will be found now in exactly the same way that the unit cells in the monoclinic, rhombohedral, and cubic systems were discovered.

TYPE 8: $a = b \neq c, \alpha = \beta = \gamma = 90°$
Essential symmetry : one 4-fold rotation axis parallel to the c axis of the unit cell.
Crystal system   : tetragonal because of the existence of the 4-fold axis.
Lattice points   : the unit cell is primitive P and contains a single lattice point.

TYPE 9: $a = b = c, \alpha = \beta \neq \gamma$
Essential symmetry : one 4-fold rotation axis parallel to the C face diagonal.
Crystal system   : tetragonal because of the 4-fold axis.
The preferable unit cell for identifying the location of the 4-fold rotation axis in the space lattice is shown by light lines in Figure 55. This unit cell is the usual tetragonal cell with parameters a', a', and c' but is clearly non-primitive, having lattice points at the corners and also at the geometrical centre — the cell is body centred.
Lattice points   : the unit cell is body centred I and contains two lattice points.

TYPE 10: $a \neq b \neq c, \alpha = \beta = \gamma = 90°$
Essential symmetry : three 2-fold rotation axes parallel to the three edges of the cell.
Crystal system   : orthorhombic since there are three 2-fold axes at right angles to one another.
Lattice points   : the unit cell is primitive P and contains one lattice point.

TYPE 11: $a = b \neq c, \alpha = \beta = 90° \neq \gamma$
Essential symmetry : three 2-fold rotation axes, one parallel to the c edge of the cell, the others parallel to the diagonals of the C face and necessarily at right angles to one another since $a = b$.

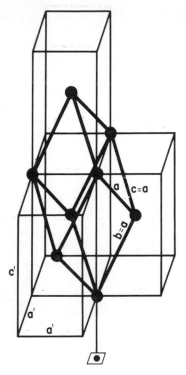

Figure 55. Diagram showing that the space lattice represented by the general unit cell (heavy lines) having parameters $a = b = c$, $\alpha = \beta \neq \gamma$ has a 4-fold rotation axis parallel to a C face diagonal and so is better represented by the body centred tetragonal unit cell (light lines) with parameters a', a', and c'

Crystal system   :   orthorhombic since there are three 2-fold axes at right angles to one another.

The unit cell which best identifies the location of the three 2-fold axes is that shown by heavy lines in Figure 56. This cell is clearly a C base centred orthorhombic cell with parameters a', b', and $c' = c$.

Lattice points   :   the unit cell is base centred C and contains two lattice points.

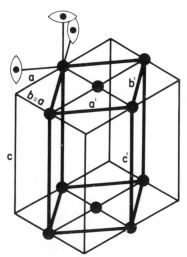

Figure 56. Diagram showing that the space lattice represented by the general unit cell (light lines) having parameters $a = b \neq c$, $\alpha = \beta = 90° \neq \gamma$ has 2-fold rotation axes parallel to the C face diagonals and another 2-fold axis parallel to the c edge and so is better represented by the base centred orthorhombic unit cell (heavy lines) with parameters a', b', and $c' = c$

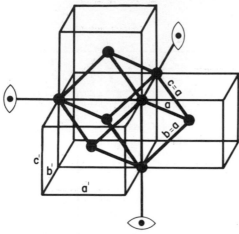

Figure 57. Diagram showing that the space
lattice represented by the general unit cell
(heavy lines) having parameters $a = b = c$,
$\alpha \neq \beta \neq \gamma$ has a 2-fold rotation axis parallel
to one of the diagonals in each of the A, B,
and C faces and so is better represented by
the body centred orthorhombic unit cell
(light lines) with parameters a', b', and c'

TYPE 12: $a = b = c, \alpha \neq \beta \neq \gamma$

Essential symmetry : three 2-fold rotation axes, each parallel to one of the A, B, and C face diagonals.

Crystal system : orthorhombic since there are three 2-fold axes which are at right angles to one another.

The best unit cell for identifying the location of the three 2-fold axes is shown by light lines in Figure 57 and is clearly a body centred orthorhombic cell with parameters a', b', and c'.

Lattice points : the unit cell is body centred I and contains two lattice points.

TYPE 13: $a = b \neq c, \alpha = \beta \neq \gamma$

Essential symmetry : three 2-fold rotation axes, two of which are parallel to the diagonals of the C face (and at right angles to one another since $a = b$), while the other passes through the cell at right angles to the C face.

Crystal system : orthorhombic since there are three 2-fold axes at right angles to one another.

The three 2-fold axes occur only for a special relationship between the angles α and γ. This relationship is

$$\cos \alpha = \frac{a}{2c} \ (1 + \cos \gamma)$$

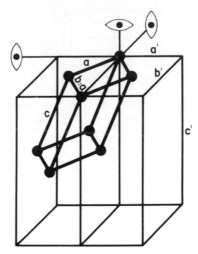

Figure 58. Diagram showing that the space lattice represented by the general unit cell (heavy lines) having parameters $a = b \neq c$, $\alpha = \beta \neq \gamma$ has a 2-fold rotation axis parallel to each of the C face diagonals with another through the cell and so is better represented by the face centred orthorhombic unit cell (light lines) with parameters a', b', and c'

and the best unit cell for identifying the location of the axes is shown by light lines in Figure 58. The cell is face centred orthorhombic with parameters a', b', and c'.

Lattice points   : the unit cell is face centred F and contains four lattice points.

TYPE 14: $a = b \neq c, \alpha = \beta = 90°, \gamma = 120°$

Essential symmetry : one 6-fold rotation axis parallel to the c edge of the unit cell.
Crystal system   : hexagonal because of the 6-fold axis.
Lattice points   : the unit cell is primitive and contains one lattice point.

    The symbol which should be used to denote this cell is the usual symbol P for a primitive cell but sometimes the letter C is used for, as shown in Figure 59, it is possible to describe the space lattice with a base centred orthorhombic unit cell. This cell is special in that $b = \sqrt{3}\,a$ and consequently the c edge becomes a 6-fold axis as required for the hexagonal system.

    It has now been demonstrated that fourteen different unit cells, the fourteen different space lattices, can be derived from a study of the symmetry that is generated when the edges and included angles of the general triclinic unit cell have all possible special values. Thus the cells derived as TYPES 1−7 , together with the two tetragonal cells (P and I), four orthorhombic cells (P, C, I, and F), and one

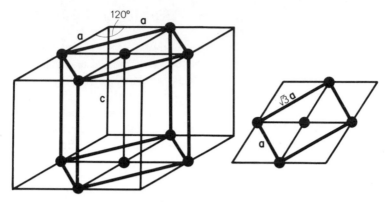

Figure 59. Diagrams showing that the hexagonal space lattice with parameters a and c can be represented by a base centred orthorhombic unit cell with parameters a, b = $\sqrt{3}$ a, and c

hexagonal cell (P) derived as TYPES 8–14 identify all possible space lattices. These space lattices are

TRICLINIC	:	P
MONOCLINIC	:	P and C
ORTHORHOMBIC	:	P, C, I, and F
RHOMBOHEDRAL	:	P
HEXAGONAL	:	P
TETRAGONAL	:	P and I
CUBIC	:	P, I, and F

It is interesting to note that these fourteen space lattices are by no means a recent discovery. The mathematicians and crystallographers of the early 19th century knew of them but the first rigorous demonstration of their existence was made by the French physicist and crystallographer Auguste Bravais, probably in 1848. It is in his honour that these fourteen different arrangements of points in space are known as the BRAVAIS LATTICES.

DEFINITION No. 36. A BRAVAIS LATTICE IS ONE OF THE FOURTEEN DIFFERENT WAYS IN WHICH IT IS POSSIBLE FOR POINTS TO OCCUR IN SPACE IN CONFORMITY WITH THE REQUIREMENTS OF A SPACE LATTICE.

All Bravais lattices are space lattices and any space lattice necessarily must be one of the fourteen Bravais lattices.

To demonstrate that all special cases of the general triclinic unit cell generate one of the fourteen Bravais lattices and no others is certainly a monumental task well beyond the scope of this book. However, there is another approach to the problem of establishing that there are no arrays of points constituting a space lattice additional to the arrays described by the Bravais lattices.

This approach makes use of the two features of space lattices specified by DEFINITION No. 32 and CONCEPT No. 55 that there are seven crystal systems and four different kinds of unit cell—base centred, body centred, face centred, and primitive. The existence of seven systems and four kinds of unit cell suggests that there are potentially $7 \times 4 = 28$ different Bravais lattices. However of these only fourteen are actually different from one another – the lattices that have just been derived; the other fourteen are redundant as now will be demonstrated.

Consider the cubic system. It has been seen that the primitive, the face centred, and the body centred unit cells describe three different space lattices of this system, but why is there no base centred cubic Bravais lattice?

The answer to this question is shown in Figure 60. Since the three pairs of faces of the cubic unit cell are identical, base centring on the A faces, the B faces or the C faces are equivalent operations and a pair of cells centred on a pair of any of these faces is shown in (a). The important effect of this centring operation on the symmetry is shown in (b) which is a view along a body diagonal of a unit cell. In the absence of the base centring points this diagonal and the other three identical body diagonals are 3-fold axes as required by the essential symmetry of the cubic system. However, in the presence of the base centring points these four 3-fold axes are changed to 1-fold axes (as can be seen in Figure 60(b)), and the space lattice described by this arrangement of lattice points cannot be classified into the cubic system. So, what is the crystal system of the 'base centred cubic' array of points if it is not cubic? To answer this question it is necessary to note that, in the absence of the base centring points, each of the axes x, y, and z parallel to the (primitive) cell edges would be a 4-fold rotation axis, but it is easy to see (Figure 60(a)) that, in the presence of the base centring points, only the z edge remains a 4-fold axis, the other two being converted to 2-fold axes. Thus the system is identified as tetragonal by the existence of the essential symmetry of one 4-fold rotation axis. The unit cell that is simplest and adequately locates the 4-fold axis is shown in (c). This new unit cell has two equal edges a' and a third edge c $(= a)$ all at right angles to one another as required for the tetragonal system, and since the new cell edges are related to the original cube there exists a simple relationship between them. Note that the edge a' is half the length of a face diagonal of the cube so that $a' = a/\sqrt{2}$, and also that the length of the c edge of the tetragonal cell is equal to a.

The tetragonal unit cell has lattice points only at the corners and is consequently a primitive unit cell. Thus, the array of points in space generated by base centring a primitive cubic unit cell (with parameter a) is properly described by a primitive tetragonal unit cell with $a' = a/\sqrt{2}$ and $c = a$ since the essential symmetry is one 4-fold rotation axis.

This analysis shows that there can be only three Bravais lattices in the cubic system – the primitive, the face centred, and the body centred; a base centred cubic space lattice cannot exist.

The same kind of analysis will now be applied to the other crystal systems.

First consider the tetragonal system to see why there is no base centred Bravais lattice and also why there is no face centred Bravais lattice.

The diagram shown in Figure 61(a) identifies the relevant lattice points of a

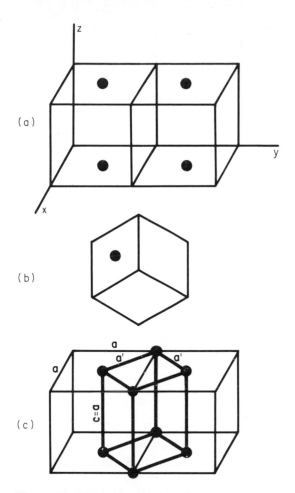

Figure 60. Diagrams showing that the addition of base centring points to a primitive cubic space lattice converts it to a primitive tetragonal space lattice

tetragonal cell centred on the C face and the primitive cell that more simply represents the same space lattice. Thus it is evident that the C base centred tetragonal Bravais lattice is redundant since it differs in no way from the primitive tetragonal lattice, but note that the parameter a' of the primitive cell is related to the parameter a of the base centred cell $a' = a/\sqrt{2}$ as indicated in (b).

Figure 61(c) shows that as a consequence of centring on either the A or the B faces of a tetragonal cell the axis xy becomes a 2-fold rotation axis and the essential 4-fold rotational symmetry of the tetragonal system is thereby destroyed. The essential symmetry of the new arrangement of points is three 2-fold axes at right angles to one another and so the crystal system is orthorhombic even though the dimensions of the A or B base centred unit cell are $a = b \neq c$.

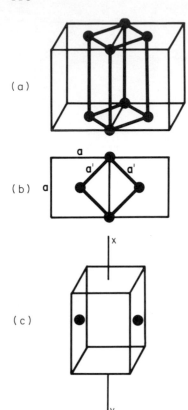

(a)

(b)

(c)

Figure 61. Diagrams showing in (a) and (b) the equivalence of the space lattices for C base centred tetragonal (light lines), and primitive tetragonal (heavy lines), and in (c) that A or B base centring converts the 4-fold rotation axis to a 2-fold axis and the space lattice becomes base centred orthorhombic

Now examine Figure 62(a) which shows two unit cells having parameters a, a, and c of a face centred tetragonal arrangement of points. Note that for clarity not all of the face centring points are shown in the two cells and that the array can be better described by the alternative unit cell which has edges a$'$, a$'$, and c all at right angles with a$' = a/\sqrt{2}$ (Figure 62(b)). It is evident that the lattice points are located at the corners and at the geometrical centre of this alternative cell which therefore is a body centred tetragonal unit cell. Thus, it is seen that the body centred tetragonal I and the face centred tetragonal F Bravais lattices are identical and it is by convention that the smaller body centred cell is usually used to represent the lattice.

This examination has shown that only two Bravais lattices exist in the tetragonal system, the primitive and the body centred. The C base centred and F face centred unit cells represent those same two lattices while the A or B base centred cell has the symmetry of the orthorhombic system.

For the rhombohedral system the essential 3-fold rotation axis is destroyed by A, B, or C base centring as shown in Figure 63 which is a view along the long body diagonal of the unit cell. Clearly, after base centring, this diagonal is not a 3-fold rotation axis (but a 1-fold axis) and since the cell has no rotational symmetry at all the lattice must be classified in the triclinic system.

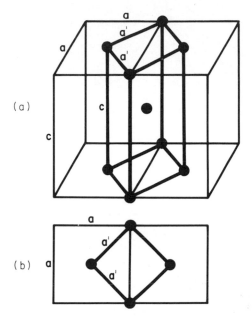

(a)

(b)

Figure 62. Diagrams showing the equivalence of the face centred (light lines) and body centred (heavy lines) space lattices in the tetragonal system

Neither face centring nor body centring the rhombohedral unit cell produces a new space lattice, for within each such centred cell a simpler, smaller, primitive rhombohedral cell exists, as is shown in Figures 64 and 65 respectively. In Figure 64 the 3-fold axis of the F and P cells is clearly xy and the three unit translations of the P cell are half the long diagonals of the identical faces of the F cell. In Figure 65 the 3-fold axis of the I cell (light lines) is xy parallel to x'y' in the P cell (heavy lines) and the unit translations of the P cell are equal to half the length of the short body diagonals of the I cell.

Thus, only the primitive space lattice occurs in the rhombohedral system.

In the hexagonal system the essential symmetry is one 6-fold rotation axis parallel to the c translation of the unit cell. This axis is shown in plan view in Figure 66(a). Figures 66(b) and (c) show the effect on this axis of base centring on the C face and on the A or B faces respectively. In the case of C base centring (b)

Figure 63. Diagram along the 3-fold axis of a rhombohedral unit cell showing that the essential symmetry is destroyed by the presence of base centring points

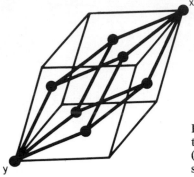

Figure 64. Diagram showing the equivalence of the face centred (light lines) and primitive (heavy lines) space lattices in the rhombohedral system

shows that the 6-fold axis becomes a 2-fold axis and the essential symmetry becomes the three 2-fold axes at right angles of the (primitive) orthorhombic system. The C face of the appropriate orthorhombic unit cell is shown by the light lines in the diagram. In the case of A or B base centring, the 6-fold axis becomes a 2-fold axis and since all other rotational symmetry disappears the space lattice becomes (base centred) monoclinic.

Similarly, for either body centring or face centring the essential 6-fold rotation axis of the hexagonal system is changed to a 2-fold axis and the essential symmetry becomes the three 2-fold axes at right angles to one another of the orthorhombic system. Figures 67(a) and (b) show respectively the body and face centring points that change the 6-fold axis in the primitive cell to a 2-fold axis in the centred cell. It

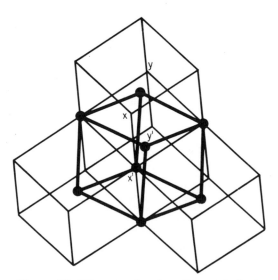

Figure 65. Diagram showing the equivalence of the body centred (light lines) and primitive (heavy lines) space lattices in the rhombohedral system

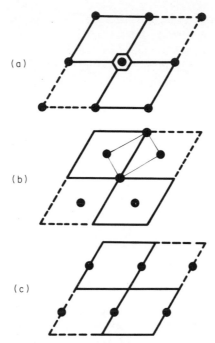

Figure 66. Diagrams showing: (a) the 6-fold rotation axis perpendicular to the C face of a hexagonal space lattice; (b) that C base centring changes the 6-fold axis to a 2-fold axis; and (c) that A or B base centring by additional points $c/2$ below the C face changes the 6-fold rotation axis to a 2-fold axis and destroys all other rotational symmetry

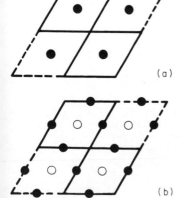

Figure 67. Diagrams of the C face showing that (a) body centring and (b) face centring a hexagonal unit cell changes the 6-fold rotation axis to a 2-fold axis and the system becomes orthorhombic. In these diagrams the centring points $c/2$ below the C face are shown filled while those in the C face are shown open

114

is instructive to draw diagrams to show that the body centring operation produces a face centred orthorhombic space lattice and that the face centring operation produces a body centred orthorhombic space lattice.

Thus, it is concluded that in the hexagonal system each centring operation changes the essential 6-fold rotation axis to a 2-fold axis and the crystal system changes to orthorhombic except for A or B base centring in which cases the symmetry is reduced to that of the monoclinic system. Consequently there can be only the primitive space lattice in the hexagonal system.

In the monoclinic system the non-primitive lattice may be either A or C base centred, depending on the way in which the axes are labelled, although by convention the C face is generally used for this space lattice. A monoclinic unit cell having parameters **a**, **b**, and **c**, centred on the B face is identical with the simpler primitive cell having parameters **a**′, **b**′, and **c**′ as shown in Figure 68(a) with the essential 2-fold axis parallel to the **b**′ (= **b**) translation, Figure 68(b). Further, the space lattices produced by either body centring or face centring a monoclinic unit

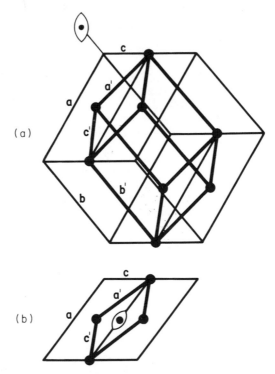

Figure 68. Diagrams showing: (a) the equivalence of the B (or A) base centred (light lines) and primitive (heavy lines) space lattices in the monoclinic system; and (b) the existence of the 2-fold rotational symmetry perpendicular to the B face, i.e. parallel to the **b**′ = **b** translation

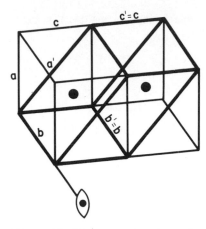

Figure 69. Diagram showing the equivalence of the body centred (light lines) and C base centred (heavy lines) space lattices in the monoclinic system

cell having parameters **a**, **b**, and **c** can be represented by a C base centred cell with parameters **a′**, **b′**, and **c′** as shown in Figures 69 and 70. In both cases the **b** translation and the **b′** translation are identical, thus preserving the identity of the essential 2-fold rotational symmetry of the monoclinic system.

Thus, it is concluded that in the monoclinic system only primitive and C base centred cells are necessary to represent all arrays of points having the essential 2-fold rotation axis.

In the triclinic system only the primitive unit cell is required, for as there is no symmetry to be identified, there is no advantage to be gained in using any of the non-primitive cells in preference to the smaller primitive cell.

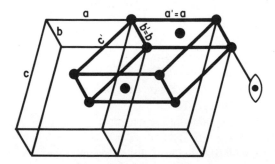

Figure 70. Diagram showing the equivalence of the face centred (light lines) and C base centred (heavy lines) space lattices in the monoclinic system

This study of the complete range of possible Bravais lattices has shown that the

cubic	A, B, and C
tetragonal	A, B, C, and F
rhombohedral	A, B, C, I, and F
hexagonal	A, B, C, I, and F
triclinic	A, B, C, I, and F

lattices are either not possible because of lowered symmetry or not necessary because of duplication.

By this elimination only the 14 Bravais lattices derived from the study of the special cases of the general triclinic unit cell remain as the different ways in which it is possible for points to occur in space in conformity with the requirements of a space lattice.

CONCEPT No. 56.   THE 14 BRAVAIS LATTICES ARE THE TRICLINIC P, THE MONOCLINIC P AND C, THE ORTHORHOMBIC P, C, I, AND F, THE RHOMBOHEDRAL P, THE HEXAGONAL P, THE TETRAGONAL P AND I, AND THE CUBIC P, I, AND F.

It is evident that all crystals have a space lattice that must be one of the 14 Bravais lattices, for these are the only ways in which indistinguishable points can occur in the three dimensions of space.

CONCEPT No. 57.   EVERY CRYSTAL HAS A SPACE LATTICE WHICH MUST BE ONE OF THE 14 BRAVAIS LATTICES.

The following are examples of a few crystals having the various Bravais lattices.

TRICLINIC   : PRIMITIVE
                copper sulphate (chalcanthite, bluestone or blue vitreol), turquoise, albite, sodium bisulphate.
MONOCLINIC   : PRIMITIVE
                malachite, azurite.
MONOCLINIC   : BASE CENTRED
                gypsum, muscovite (mica), borax.
ORTHORHOMBIC : PRIMITIVE
                topaz, aragonite, marcasite.
ORTHORHOMBIC : BASE CENTRED
                chlorine, iodine, gallium, uranium.
ORTHORHOMBIC : BODY CENTRED
                thorium tetrafluoride.
ORTHORHOMBIC : FACE CENTRED
                sulphur, zirconium sulphate, plutonium.

RHOMBOHEDRAL : PRIMITIVE
quartz, corundum (ruby or sapphire), arsenic, antimony, tourmaline, calcite, magnesite, graphite, haematite, mercury.

HEXAGONAL : PRIMITIVE
zinc, cadmium, titanium, magnesium, beryl (aquamarine and emerald), apatite.

TETRAGONAL : PRIMITIVE
rutile, cassiterite.

TETRAGONAL : BODY CENTRED
zircon, tin, indium.

CUBIC : PRIMITIVE
polonium, pyrites, caesium chloride, sodium chlorate.

CUBIC : BODY CENTRED
iron, chromium, sodium, potassium, tungsten, vanadium.

CUBIC : FACE CENTRED
sodium chloride (common salt or halite), copper, silver, gold, diamond, spinel, garnet, fluorite.

Chapter 15

Crystal Structures

Having now seen that the scheme of repetition of the motifs of any crystal must be described by one of the fourteen Bravais lattices with a unit cell having the parameters **a**, **b**, **c**, α, β, and γ it remains only to specify the array of atoms in the motif to complete the description of the arrangement of atoms in that crystal.

The motif may contain one or more atoms of one or more elements so that the description of the motif obviously involves the specification of the identity of each atom and its location in relation to the lattice point. The locations of the various atoms in each motif are invariably given by the fractional coordinates of the sites defined previously in DEFINITION Nos. 16 and 15.

DEFINITION No. 16. The fractional coordinates of any point within a unit cell are the coordinates of that point represented as fractions of the unit translations specifying the edges of the unit cell.

DEFINITION No. 15. The coordinates of any point in a unit cell are the distances, measured from the origin to the intersections with the edges, of lines drawn parallel to them through the point.

Also CONCEPT No. 28 should be remembered.

CONCEPT No. 28. The fractional coordinates of a point within a unit cell are independent of the absolute values of the unit translations and of the angle between them.

This concept is as true for three-dimensional patterns as it is for the two-dimensional case for which it was evolved in Chapter 5.

At this stage it is useful to determine the fractional coordinates of some important points in a unit cell having parameters **a**, **b**, and **c** as shown in Figure 71. The lattice parameters are the unit translations that identify the x, y, and z axes which together with the intersection at point g constitute the frame of reference for the determination of the fractional coordinates of all points within the cell.

Consider the point h halfway between g and a along the x axis. This point has coordinates of $a/2$ on the x axis and zero on the other two axes; the coordinates are $a/2, 0, 0$. The fractional coordinates are obtained by dividing each coordinate by the appropriate lattice parameter, that is the appropriate unit translation. Thus the

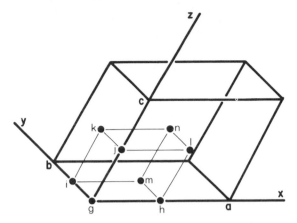

Figure 71. An arbitrary unit cell with parameters
a, b, and c, corner point g, edge centre points h, i,
and j, face centre points k, l, and m, and body
centre point n

fractional coordinates for the point h are a/2a, 0/b, 0/c which clearly reduce to
½, 0, 0.

Similarly the point i has coordinates 0, b/2, 0 and therefore the fractional
coordinates are 0, ½, 0 and the point j has fractional coordinates of 0, 0, ½.

The point k is in the centre of the A face of the unit cell and has coordinates of
zero on the x axis, b/2 on the y axis and c/2 on the z axis. The fractional
coordinates obtained by dividing by the unit translations are 0/a, b/2b, c/2c, that is
0, ½, ½ and similarly the fractional coordinates of the points l and m in the centres
of the B and C faces are ½, 0, ½ and ½, ½, 0 respectively. Finally, the point n in the
geometrical centre of the cell has coordinates a/2, b/2, c/2 and therefore the
fractional coordinates are ½, ½, ½. The fractional coordinates of all other points in
the cell are calculated in the same way by first finding the coordinates of the point
in terms of the three unit translations then dividing by the unit translations to
obtain the three fractions as required.

For crystals having a single atom motif, each atom is considered to be a sphere
invariably centred on the lattice points so that the fractional coordinates of the
atoms in the unit cell are identical with the fractional coordinates of the lattice
points in the unit cell. Note that for this case the crystal consists of an array of one
kind of atom only and the material of the crystal must be an element.

CONCEPT No. 58.   FOR CRYSTALS HAVING A MOTIF CONSISTING OF A
SINGLE ATOM, THAT ATOM IS LOCATED AT THE
POINTS OF THE APPROPRIATE SPACE LATTICE.

It is instructive to examine the arrangements of atoms in crystals of this kind for
the four different types of Bravais lattice.

1. PRIMITIVE BRAVAIS LATTICE.

The primitive unit cell contains a single lattice point, see DEFINITION No. 6. This point is regarded as being the point at the origin of the axis system, i.e. the point g in Figure 71, which being at the origin has fractional coordinates 0, 0, 0 and so the single atom associated with each unit cell is located at the point 0, 0, 0. This follows from CONCEPT No. 27.

CONCEPT No. 27.　　The motif or part thereof located at the lattice point of a primitive unit cell has the fractional coordinates 0, 0,

This becomes, for the three-dimensional case, CONCEPT No. 59 below.

CONCEPT No. 59.　　THE MOTIF OR PART THEREOF LOCATED AT THE LATTICE POINT OF A PRIMITIVE UNIT CELL HAS THE FRACTIONAL COORDINATES 0, 0, 0.

Few crystals have a primitive Bravais lattice and single atom motif, but two are the metals mercury and polonium.

MERCURY — Bravais lattice: primitive rhombohedral

parameters (at $-40°$C): $a(= b = c) = 300.5$ pm

$$\alpha(= \beta = \gamma) = 70°31'$$

motif:　　one mercury atom located at 0, 0, 0

Thus the crystal structure of mercury, which freezes at $-39°$C, is primitive rhombohedral with the specified lattice parameters and with mercury atoms located at the corners of the unit cell, i.e. at the 0, 0, 0 points.

POLONIUM — Bravais lattice: primitive cubic

parameter: $a(= b = c) = 334$ pm

motif:　　one polonium atom located at 0, 0, 0

The crystal structure of the rare metallic element polonium is primitive cubic with $a = 334$ pm and single polonium atoms located at the corners of the unit cell.

2. BASE CENTRED BRAVAIS LATTICE.

The A, B, or C base centred Bravais lattices has lattice points at the corners of the unit cell with additional points in the centres of an opposite pair of faces as specified by DEFINITION No. 33.

DEFINITION No. 33. A base centred unit cell has lattice points at the cell corners and, in addition, at the centres of two opposite faces.

Thus, there are two lattice points associated with each unit cell, one corner point and one base centring point. In turn this means that there are two motifs in each unit cell, one at each lattice point.

For a crystal having such a Bravais lattice and a motif of one atom, the structure would be described by the appropriate parameters a, b, c, α, β, and γ with the two atoms in the unit cell located at 0, 0, 0 and ½, ½, 0 (for C base centring); the 0, 0, 0 atom of course being located at the cell corner and the ½, ½, 0 atom being in the centre of the C face. If the cell was B base centred the fractional coordinates of the face centring atom would be ½, 0, ½ and if A base centred it would be 0, ½, ½.

There is no material (element) having a single atom motif on the points of a base centred Bravais lattice but note that if it did exist a crystal with this kind of structure would necessarily be orthorhombic or monoclinic since these are the only two crystal systems in which base centred Bravais lattices occur.

3. BODY CENTRED BRAVAIS LATTICE.

Body centred Bravais lattices have lattice points at the corners of the unit cell as well as at the geometrical centre of the cell.

DEFINITION No. 34. A body centred unit cell has lattice points at each corner and an additional point at the geometrical centre.

Such cells contain two points, one at the corner and one at the body centre, the fractional coordinates of them being 0, 0, 0 and ½, ½, ½ respectively. For a single atom motif the unit cell contains two atoms, one at each point, and there are many elements, of which the following are two examples, with this kind of structure.

TIN   — Bravais lattice: body centred tetragonal
           parameters: a(= b) = 583 pm, c = 318 pm
           motif: one tin atom; locations 0, 0, 0 and ½, ½, ½

SODIUM — Bravais lattice: body centred cubic
           parameter: a(= b = c) = 429 pm
           motif: one sodium atom; locations 0, 0, 0 and ½, ½, ½

4. FACE CENTRED BRAVAIS LATTICE.

The face centred Bravais lattices have lattice points at the cell corners and in the centres of each face.

DEFINITION No. 35. A face centred unit cell has lattice points at each corner and additional points at the geometrical centre of each of the six faces.

There are four points in the cell, the corner point and three face centring points. A crystal with a single atom motif is described by the cell parameters with the four atoms in the cell located at the sites of the points — 0, 0, 0 for the corner point,

0, ½, ½ for the A face centring point, ½, 0, ½ for the B face centring point, and ½, ½, 0 for the C face centring point. Two elements having this structure are the metals copper and gold.

COPPER — Bravais lattice: face centred cubic
           parameter: $a(= b = c) = 361$ pm
           motif: one copper atom; locations 0, 0, 0 , 0, ½, ½, ½, 0, ½, and ½, ½, 0

GOLD   — Bravais lattice: face centred cubic
           parameter: $a(= b = c) = 408$ pm
           motif: one gold atom; locations 0, 0, 0 , 0, ½, ½ , ½, 0, ½, and ½, ½, 0

The structures described so far have been very simple but for crystals having a motif composed of a more complex array of atoms the means of describing that complex structure is identical with the means used to describe the simple structures. The size and shape of the unit cell is specified by the lattice parameters **a, b, c,** α, β, and γ and the location in the cell of each atom in the motifs is specified by the appropriate fractional coordinates.

As an example of a slightly more complex structure consider the metal zinc.

The Bravais lattice is hexagonal — remember it is necessarily primitive with one

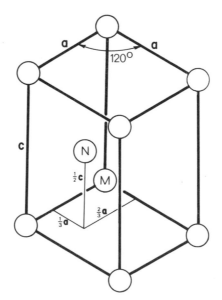

Figure 72. Diagram of the hexagonal unit cell for zinc with **a** = 267 pm, **c** = 495 pm and the two atoms M and N of the motif located at the sites 0, 0, 0 and 2/3, 1/3, 1/2 respectively

lattice point in each unit cell. For zinc the lattice parameters are a (= b) = 267 pm and c = 495 pm, and the motif consists of two zinc atoms, one located at the cell corner 0, 0, 0 and the other located within the cell at the site 2/3, 1/3, 1/2 as shown in Figure 72. One of the atoms (M) is located at the lattice point (0, 0, 0) while the other (N) within the cell is part of the motif and therefore necessarily associated with the lattice point at 0, 0, 0.

The structure specified by the parameters a and c of the hexagonal unit cell with identical atoms at the sites 0, 0, 0 and 1/3, 2/3, 1/2 also occurs for other elements such as magnesium, cadmium, and titanium. This structure is termed CLOSE PACKED HEXAGONAL or HEXAGONAL CLOSE PACKED for it represents one of two different ways in which the atoms, considered to be spheres, are packed together as tightly as is possible geometrically. The other structure in which the atoms are CLOSE PACKED is the FACE CENTRED CUBIC arrangment of single atom motifs. Detailed descriptions of these two structures and the properties of them are given in many books dealing with the elements of crystallography and will not be repeated here.

In crystals which contain more than one kind of atom the identity and location of each in the unit cell must be specified. Three representative examples, two primitive and one non-primitive, will be now examined.

First consider the mineral rutile, titanium dioxide TiO_2 which has a primitive tetragonal Bravais lattice with parameters a = 459 pm and c = 296 pm. The motif is two TiO_2 molecules, that is two titanium atoms and four oxygen atoms. Thus the motif for this crystal consists of six atoms and the fractional coordinates of these six atoms are

titanium: 0, 0, 0 and 0.5, 0.5, 0.5
oxygen: 0.3, 0.3, 0 , 0.7, 0.7, 0 , 0.2, 0.8, 0.5, and 0.8, 0.2, 0.5

This structure is shown in Figure 73. The titanium atoms A and B are located at the easily identifiable locations 0, 0, 0 and 0.5, 0.5, 0.5 respectively. The oxygen atoms are a little more difficult to locate. Atoms C and D lie in the C face of the cell since the fractional coordinate on the c axis is zero. Thus

atom C is located at 0.3, 0.3, 0 and
atom D is located at 0.7, 0.7, 0.

These atoms are shown in the bottom surface of the cell because the corner A has been selected as the origin for the system of axes. Since a unit cell of a crystal is completely representative of it, the atom arrangement in opposite faces must be identical and therefore the top face of the unit cell also contains two oxygen atoms having equivalent positions to the atoms C and D. These two atoms in the top face are associated with the adjacent unit cell and consequently do not constitute part of the motif of structure in the cell shown in the diagram.

The other two oxygen atoms in the unit cell lie midway between the two C faces since the fractional coordinate on the c axis is 0.5. Thus

atom E is located at 0.2, 0.8, 0.5 and
atom F is located at 0.8, 0.2, 0.5.

124

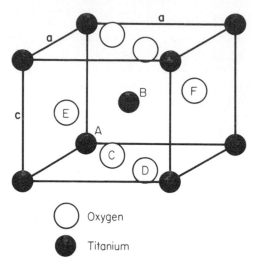

Figure 73. Diagram of the primitive tetragonal unit cell of rutile

Note that the unit cell, being primitive tetragonal, contains a single lattice point at 0, 0, 0. One of the two titanium atoms is located at this point, the other titanium atom and the four oxygen atoms constitute the remainder of the one motif that the unit cell contains. This complete motif is associated with the point 0, 0, 0 even though five of the six atoms of the motif are distributed throughout the cell.

Next consider the crystal structure of the compound caesium chloride, CsCl shown in Figure 74(a). The unit cell is a cube with edge length a = 412 pm and it might appear that the Bravais lattice is body centred since there are atoms at the corners of the cell as well as at the geometrical centre. However, this is not true. For the Bravais lattice to be body centred the motif at the sites 0, 0, 0 and ½, ½, ½ must be identical. As is shown clearly in Figure 74(a) there is a caesium atom at the 0, 0, 0 site but a chlorine atom at the ½, ½, ½ site so that obviously both sites cannot be lattice points. Only one of the two sites can be a lattice point and by convention this is the site 0, 0, 0. One lattice point in the unit cell means that it is a primitive unit cell and so the Bravais lattice is primitive cubic. The motif must comprise the CsCl molecule with the caesium atom located at the lattice point and the chlorine atom at the centre of the cell at the site ½, ½, ½.

In this structure the caesium atoms occur in space at the corners of a simple cube and similarly the chlorine atoms occur in space at the corners of a simple cube. The two cubes have identical edge lengths (a = 412 pm), and as shown in Figure 74(b) are displaced relative to one another such that a corner of one cube is the centre of the other. For this reason the structure is sometimes referred to as consisting of two interpenetrating simple cubic arrays of atoms.

A material with a complex non-primitive crystal structure is common salt – sodium chloride – NaCl. This material is face centred cubic with parameter

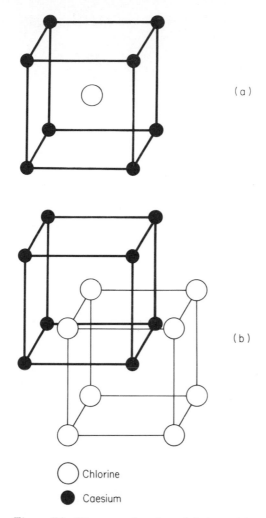

(a)

(b)

Chlorine

Caesium

Figure 74. Diagrams showing: (a) the cubic
unit cell of caesium chloride with parameter
a = 412 pm; and (b) the concept of two
interpenetrating primitive cubic arrays of the
two different atoms

a = 563 pm and a motif of one NaCl molecule, that is one atom of sodium and one
atom of chlorine is associated with each lattice point. Since there are four lattice
points in the face centred cell there must be four molecules in the cell, one
molecule (motif) at each point. Thus the cell contains eight atoms, four sodium
atoms, and four chlorine atoms. The most convenient way to describe the location
of these eight atoms is to consider that the sodium atoms are located at the corner
and face centring sites. This means that for the system of axes x, y, z shown in

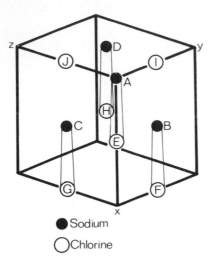

● Sodium

○ Chlorine

Figure 75. The face centred cubic unit cell of sodium chloride with parameter $a = 563$ pm and the four motifs comprising the pairs of atoms A–E, B–F, C–G, and D–H

Figure 75 the fractional coordinates of the sodium atoms are:

atom A at 0, 0, 0
atom B at ½, ½, 0
atom C at ½, 0, ½
atom D at 0, ½, ½

Since each motif in the structure must be exactly the same, the relationship between the sodium atom and the chlorine atom in each molecule (motif) must be identical. One possible relationship is shown in Figure 75, but inspection will reveal that many different pairings are possible. The pairings shown are:

sodium atom A with chlorine atom E,
sodium atom B with chlorine atom F,
sodium atom C with chlorine atom G, and
sodium atom D with chlorine atom H.

With the (sodium) atom A at the origin 0, 0, 0 of the axes the fractional coordinates of the chlorine atoms must be:

atom E at ½, 0, 0
atom F at 1, ½, 0
atom G at 1, 0, ½
atom H at ½, ½, ½

However, this specification is not used often even though it describes a consistent relationship between the two atoms in each motif. The specification of the locations of the chlorine atoms can be simplified by noting that the atom I is exactly equivalent to the atom F and the atom J is exactly equivalent to the atom G. Thus the set of chlorine atoms with simplest fractional coordinates, i.e. the set

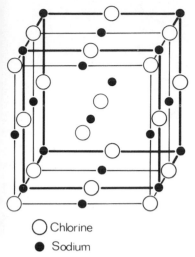

○ Chlorine

● Sodium

Figure 76. Diagram showing that the structure of sodium chloride can be represented as two interpenetrating face centred cubic arrays with sodium atoms comprising one (heavy lines) and chlorine atoms comprising the other (light lines)

E, I, J, H is generally used despite the absence of a constant relationship between the four sodium atoms A, B, C, D and these four chlorine atoms. The fractional coordinates of the chlorine atoms E, I, J, H are:

atom E at ½, 0, 0
atom I at 0, ½, 0
atom J at 0, 0, ½
atom H at ½, ½, ½

Thus, the crystal structure of sodium chloride is face centred cubic with sodium atoms located at the cell corners and in the centres of the cell faces and chlorine atoms located at the centres of the cell edges and at the centre of the cell. The complete structure is shown in Figure 76. Close examination of the diagram shows that, like caesium chloride, this structure also can be described as two interpenetrating arrays on atoms. One array is a simple face centred cubic distribution of sodium atoms (shown with heavy lines) and the other array is an identical face centred cubic distribution of chlorine atoms (shown with light lines).

It should now be evident that the structure of any crystal is specified by the size and shape of the unit cell and the identity and location within the cell of the atoms in the motifs associated with the lattice points in the cell and so

CONCEPT No. 29. The complete description of a plane pattern is given by the parameters **a**, **b**, and α of the unit cell, the size and shape of the motif, and the fractional coordinates locating the motif or motifs within the cell

can be extended to the three-dimensional pattern.

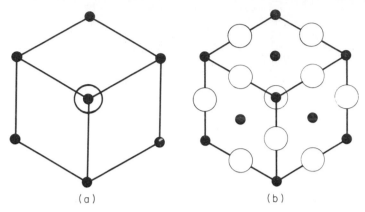

Figure 77. Diagrams showing the arrangement of atoms along the cube diagonals of the unit cells of (a) caesium chloride, and (b) sodium chloride

CONCEPT No. 60. THE PARAMETERS a, b, c, α, β, and γ OF THE UNIT CELL TOGETHER WITH THE IDENTITY AND FRACTIONAL COORDINATES OF EACH ATOM IN THE CELL COMPLETELY SPECIFIES THE STRUCTURE OF ANY CRYSTAL.

For the few representative crystals so far examined the crystal system was identified by the shape of the unit cell. However it was established in Chapter 12 that the classification of crystals into systems is based not on the cell shape but on certain essential symmetry requirements. In the cases of mercury, polonium, tin, sodium, copper, and gold the motif is a single atom located at the lattice points so that the symmetry properties of the crystal structure and of the space lattice are identical. For mercury this symmetry is a single 3-fold rotation axis so that the crystal system is necessarily rhombohedral and this is manifest in the shape of the unit cell. For tin the essential symmetry is one 4-fold rotation axis identifying it as tetragonal while polonium, sodium, copper, and gold are identified as cubic by the existence of four 3-fold axes.

The requirement that the body diagonals of the unit cells of caesium chloride and sodium chloride be 3-fold axes, and the crystal system therefore cubic, is satisfied by the array of atoms in the two structures as shown in Figure 77. Figure 77(a) shows the structure of caesium chloride as viewed along one of the four (identical) body diagonals of the unit cell with the small caesium atoms at the cell corners and the large chlorine atom at the cell centre site ½, ½, ½. Figure 77(b) similarly shows the structure of sodium chloride as seen along one of the four (identical) body diagonals with the small sodium atoms at the points of the face centred cubic Bravais lattice and the larger chlorine atoms at the edge centres and at the body centre of the unit cell. Clearly, for both structures, the body diagonals are 3-fold rotation axes and the crystal structures have the four 3-fold axes required for the cubic system.

Chapter 16

Microscopic Symmetry

Consider now the atom arrangement in the metal zinc (Figure 72) for which the Bravais lattice is hexagonal and the essential symmetry requirement is one 6-fold axis parallel to the c axis of the unit cell. A plan view of the structure is shown in Figure 78 in which the atoms are represented as spheres just touching one another. The C face of the unit cell is outlined so that the heavy circles represent atoms at the 0, 0, 0 type sites, that is, the sites at the corners of the unit cells. The light circles represent atoms at the 2/3, 1/3, 1/2 type sites lying below the atoms represented by the heavy circles, and that particular atom centred on E is the atom located in the cell with face ABCD, i.e. the atom N shown in Figure 72. The space lattice of this structure comprises the set of lattice points at which are located the atoms represented by the heavy circles in Figure 78. Such points are A, B, C, D, etc., and clearly for this lattice the c axis (normal to the diagram) through any of these points is a 6-fold rotation axis as required for the hexagonal system. However,

Figure 78. Diagram along the c axis of the hexagonal unit cell of zinc showing the C face with atoms (heavy circles) at the corners A, B, C, and D with another plane of atoms (light circles) located c/2 below the C face; the atom centred on E has the fractional coordinates 2/3, 1/3, 1/2

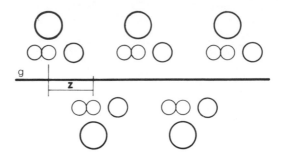

Figure 79. Diagram showing the combination of reflection and translation through distance z to produce a glide plane g perpendicular to the diagram

in the crystal structure shown in Figure 78 the presence of atoms at the 2/3, 1/3, 1/2 sites seems to indicate that the c axis is not a 6-fold axis at all but a 3-fold axis instead. It will now be shown that this is not the case and that the c axis does indeed have 6-fold symmetry as a consequence of the existence in this structure of symmetry elements other than those included in the set of macroscopic symmetry elements as defined in DEFINITION No. 30.

These additional symmetry properties relate to the detailed arrangements of atoms in crystals and for this reason are termed MICROSCOPIC SYMMETRY ELEMENTS. It will be remembered that the macroscopic symmetry elements are all associated with the point at the centre of a crystal and, having a direct influence on external shape, these symmetry elements can be deduced from a study of the shape of freely formed crystals. This is not the case with the microscopic symmetry elements for these have no influence on external shape and can be detected only by X-ray diffraction methods.

There are two kinds of microscopic symmetry element – the GLIDE PLANE and the SCREW AXIS.

Consider Figure 79 in which a plane g, normal to the diagram, would be a mirror plane except that the array of atoms above the plane and the array below the plane are displaced relative to one another by the distance (translation) z Thus, the array of atoms on either side of the plane can be generated from the other by the combined operations of mirror reflection across the plane g followed by translation through the distance z. Clearly the combined operations of reflection and translation transforms the array of atoms to self coincidence and so by DEFINITION No. 8 constitutes a symmetry operation. The operation is termed GLIDE and the plane g is termed a GLIDE PLANE.

DEFINITION No. 37. A GLIDE PLANE IS A PLANE ACROSS WHICH MIRROR REFLECTION COMBINED WITH A TRANSLATION TRANSFORMS AN ARRAY OF ATOMS TO SELF COINCIDENCE.

Glide planes have exactly the same influence on the external shape of a crystal as do mirror planes. It is most important to realize that if the point group of symmetry of a particular crystal contains a mirror plane or mirror planes then that plane or those planes may in fact be glide planes in the detailed array of atoms in the crystal.

The translation z associated with a glide plane may be only one of the following:

(a) one-half of one of the unit translations a, b, or c defining the edges of the unit cell, or

(b) one-half or one-quarter of a face diagonal.

The symbols used to represent glide plane elements of symmetry with these translations are, in the Hermann—Mauguin notation:

translation ½a	:	symbol	a
translation ½b	:	symbol	b
translation ½c	:	symbol	c
translation ½ face diagonal	:	symbol	n
translation ¼ face diagonal	:	symbol	d

Consider now Figure 80 in which the axis zz would be a 2-fold rotation axis except for the displacement $y/2$ of the atoms A relative to the atoms B. Thus the array of atoms A (or B) can be generated from the array of atoms B (or A) by a $180°$ rotation about zz followed by translation through the distance $y/2$ parallel to the axis zz. The combined effect of rotation and translation transforms the array to self coincidence and is therefore a symmetry operation. The axis about which the rotation occurs is termed a SCREW AXIS OF ROTATIONAL SYMMETRY or simply a SCREW AXIS.

DEFINITION No. 38. A SCREW AXIS OF ROTATIONAL SYMMETRY IS AN AXIS ABOUT WHICH A ROTATION COMBINED WITH A TRANSLATION PARALLEL TO THE AXIS TRANS-FORMS AN ARRAY OF ATOMS TO SELF COINCIDENCE.

Again it is important to realize that, as far as the external shape of a freely formed crystal is concerned, screw axes and rotation axes are indistinguishable. They become distinguishable only in the detailed array of atoms in a crystal structure.

Any rotation axis in a point group of symmetry of a crystal may be in fact a screw axis in the array of atoms but the translation distance associated with it depends on the multiplicity of the (apparent) rotation axis. For the screw axis shown in Figure 80 the rotation of $180°$ corresponds to a 2-fold axis and the translation $y/2$ necessarily must be one-half the distance y between lattice points in the direction of the axis which is identified by the symbol 2_1.

The screw axes which can be derived from all rotation axes are denoted by the Hermann—Mauguin symbols as follows.

Rotation axis	Translation (fraction of the distance between lattice points in the direction of the axis)	Symbol	Graphical symbol
2	1/2	2_1	
3	1/3	3_1	
3	2/3	3_2	
4	1/4	4_1	
4	1/2	4_2	
4	3/4	4_3	
6	1/6	6_1	
6	1/3	6_2	
6	1/2	6_3	
6	2/3	6_4	
6	5/6	6_5	

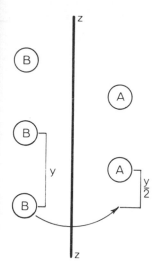

Figure 80. Diagram showing the combination of a 2-fold rotation about zz and translation through distance y/2 to produce a 2_1 screw axis

It can now be appreciated that the only symmetry elements that might be present in the structure of any crystal are the following:

rotation axes   : 1, 2, 3, 4, 6
screw axes   : $2_1, 3_1, 3_2, 4_1, 4_2, 4_3, 6_1, 6_2, 6_3, 6_4, 6_5$
rotary inversion axes: $\bar{3}, \bar{4}, \bar{6}$
centre of symmetry : $\bar{1}$
mirror plane   : m
glide planes   : a, b, c, n, d

Note that these elements are the macroscopic symmetry elements defined in DEFINITION No. 30 together with the microscopic symmetry elements that have just been examined and which may be defined as follows.

DEFINITION No. 39. THE MICROSCOPIC SYMMETRY ELEMENTS ARE THOSE SYMMETRY ELEMENTS WHICH HAVE NO INFLUENCE ON THE EXTERNAL SHAPE OF FREELY FORMED CRYSTALS, BEING CONCERNED ONLY WITH THE DETAILED ARRAY OF ATOMS WITHIN THE CRYSTAL AND, INVOLVING A TRANSLATION OPERATION, ARE DETECTABLE ONLY BY X-RAY DIFFRACTION METHODS. THE ELEMENTS COMPRISE FIVE DIFFERENT KINDS OF GLIDE PLANE AND ELEVEN DIFFERENT KINDS OF SCREW AXIS.

It is now necessary to return to the examination of the structure of zinc shown in Figure 78 to consider the array of atoms around an axis (HH) perpendicular to the diagram and passing through the point H. Figure 81 shows these atoms drawn smaller than in Figure 78 so that the arrangement of the three atoms ABC with the three atoms EFG below them may be seen clearly.

134

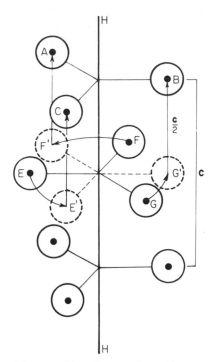

Figure 81. Perspective diagram showing that for the array of atoms in zinc, the axis HH, passing through the point H in Figure 78, is a 6_3 screw axis

The diagram indicates that a 6-fold rotation about the axis HH moves the atom E through 60° to E', the atom F through 60° to F', and the atom G through 60° to G'. A subsequent translation of c/2 parallel to HH moves the atoms at E', F', and G' to C, A, and B respectively. Clearly the array of atoms produced by the combined effect of 6-fold rotation about the axis HH and translation of c/2 parallel to HH is self coincident with the initial array. By DEFINITION No. 14 the combination of the rotation and the translation is a symmetry element, specifically the axis HH is a 6_3 screw axis. Thus the requirement that the c axis (HH) be a 6-fold axis is satisfied by the array of atoms in the crystal and materials with this structure — zinc, magnesium, cadmium, titanium, etc. — have the essential symmetry of the hexagonal system.

In the crystal structure of rutile, TiO_2, the array of atoms shown in Figure 73 would seem to contravene the requirement that the c axis be a 4-fold axis for the crystal system to be tetragonal. However the c axis is in fact a 4_2 screw axis, the requirement is satisfied, and the crystal system is indeed tetragonal.

Chapter 17

Space Groups

In previous chapters it has been established that for any particular crystal the distribution in space of the motifs of structure is described by the geometry of the array of points in the Bravais lattice of that crystal. The Bravais lattice specifies the way in which the motifs occur in a crystal but provides no information at all about the motifs.

It has been also established that at each point in the Bravais lattice there exists a collection of symmetry elements identifying the macroscopic symmetry of the array of atoms (motifs) about that point and which incidentally determines the external shape of a crystal formed without impediment. The point group of symmetry provides information about the symmetry of the array of atoms in the motif but not about the distribution of the motifs within the crystal.

Clearly, detailed information about the symmetry properties of the complete array of atoms in a crystal can be obtained only from the combined specifications of the symmetry at a lattice point (the point group modified perhaps by translational microscopic symmetry) and the distribution in space of those points (the Bravais lattice). Such a combination provides a full description of the symmetry elements in a crystal and is called a SPACE GROUP.

DEFINITION No. 40. THE SPACE GROUP OF A CRYSTAL IS THE COLLEC-
TION OF SYMMETRY ELEMENTS WHICH, DISTRI-
BUTED IN SPACE ACCORDING TO THE BRAVAIS
LATTICE, PROVIDES A DESCRIPTION OF THE TOTAL
SYMMETRY OF THE ARRAY OF ATOMS IN THE
STRUCTURE OF THAT CRYSTAL.

Since the space groups are concerned with the properties of the actual arrays of atoms in crystals the derivation of all possible space groups is more complicated than simply combining the Bravais lattices and point groups for each crystal system. Such a procedure ignores the existence of the microscopic symmetry elements so that allowance must be made for the possibility that in the detailed distribution of atoms in a crystal a macroscopic mirror plane may be a glide plane and a macroscopic rotation axis may be a screw axis.

It is instructive to derive a few space groups.

Consider first the triclinic system for which there is only one Bravais lattice, the primitive P lattice, and two point groups — 1 and $\bar{1}$. The only ways in which symmetry elements may occur in a triclinic crystal are:

(i) 1-fold rotation axes in a P lattice — specified as P1 using the Hermann–Mauguin notation, and

(ii) $\bar{1}$ centres of symmetry in a P lattice — specified as $\bar{P}1$.

These two combinations, P1 and P$\bar{1}$, are the two space groups of the triclinic system. Note that the second part of the terms indicates 1-fold rotational symmetry and therefore the triclinic system, while the first part indicates that the Bravais lattice is primitive.

Next consider the monoclinic system. In this system there are two Bravais lattices, the primitive P and the base centred C, and there are three point groups 2, m, and 2/m. However, it will be remembered that, in the detailed array of atoms that constitutes the structure of a crystal, a macroscopic mirror plane m might be a glide plane (in this case the glide plane c), while the rotation axis 2 might be a screw axis (in this case 2_1). These possibilities must be recognized in deriving the complete set of symmetry elements that can occur in the P and C Bravais lattices of the monoclinic system. The derivation is made as follows.

(i)	A 2-fold rotation axis in the P and C lattices:	P2	C2
(ii)	A 2_1 screw axis in the two lattices:	$P2_1$	$C2_1$
(iii)	A mirror plane m in the two lattices:	Pm	Cm
(iv)	A glide plane c in the two lattices:	Pc	Cc
(v)	A 2-fold axis and mirror plane m (2/m) in the two lattices:	P2/m	C2/m
(vi)	A 2_1 screw axis and mirror plane m (2_1/m) in the two lattices:	$P2_1/m$	$C2_1/m$
(vii)	A 2-fold axis and glide plane c (2/c) in the two lattices:	P2/c	C2/c
(viii)	A 2_1 screw axis and glide plane c (2_1/c) in the two lattices:	$P2_1/c$	$C2_1/c$

These sixteen combinations do not all specify different arrays of symmetry elements in space for it is possible to demonstrate that the combinations C2 and $C2_1$ are identical, the combinations C2/m and $C2_1$/m are identical, and the combinations C2/c and $C2_1$/c are identical. Thus, there are thirteen different combinations of symmetry elements that can occur in the array of atoms in a monoclinic crystal. The monoclinic system has thirteen space groups and it is most important to realize that the array of atoms in every monoclinic crystal must have symmetry properties that are described by one of these space groups. Note that the second part of the thirteen terms indicates the 2-fold rotation symmetry that identifies the monoclinic system, while the first part specifies whether the Bravais lattice is primitive P or base centred C.

In a similar way the possible combinations of symmetry elements in crystals of the other five systems can be determined. The results of such determinations show that there are:

2 space groups in the triclinic system,
13 space groups in the monoclinic system,
59 space groups in the orthorhombic system,
25 space groups in the rhombohedral system,
27 space groups in the hexagonal system,
68 space groups in the tetragonal system, and
36 space groups in the cubic system.

The total number of space groups is 230 and these are the only ways in which different distributions of compatible combinations of macroscopic and microscopic symmetry elements can occur in the array of atoms in any crystal.

As has been demonstrated, at least for the triclinic and monoclinic systems, the Hermann–Mauguin space group notation comprises a leading symbol (P, A, B, C, I, or F) which identifies the type of Bravais lattice, followed by a set of symbols that specify the complete collection of symmetry elements occurring within the array of atoms of the crystal. Remembering that crystals are classified into seven systems according to rotational symmetry, the second part of the space group notation identifies that essential symmetry and thereby also identifies the crystal system.

CONCEPT No. 61.   THE SPACE GROUP NOTATION FOR A PARTICULAR CRYSTAL COMPRISES TWO PARTS, THE FIRST IDENTIFYING THE BRAVAIS LATTICE TYPE AND THE SECOND IDENTIFYING THE TOTAL SYMMETRY OF THE ARRAY OF ATOMS IN THE CRYSTAL AND THEREFORE ALSO THE CRYSTAL SYSTEM.

In reading the space group notation it is important to remember that:

a 1-fold axis includes the elements: $1, \bar{1}$
a 2-fold axis includes the elements: $2, 2_1, m, a, b, c, n, d$
a 3-fold axis includes the elements: $3, \bar{3}, 3_1, 3_2$
a 4-fold axis includes the elements: $4, \bar{4}, 4_1, 4_2, 4_3$
a 6-fold axis includes the elements: $6, \bar{6}, 6_1, 6_2, 6_3, 6_4, 6_5$

and that the existence of

1-fold axes denote the triclinic system,
one 2-fold axis denotes the monoclinic system,
three 2-fold axes at right angles denote the orthorhombic system,
one 3-fold axis denotes the rhombohedral system,
four 3-fold axes at $70°32'$ to one another denote the cubic system,
one 4-fold axis denotes the tetragonal system, and
one 6-fold axis denotes the hexagonal system.

Further examination of the microscopic symmetry elements and of the space groups will not be pursued here, for there are many excellent books that deal with the subject at both elementary and advanced levels.

Chapter 18

Defects in Crystals

No further examination of the detailed structure of particular crystals nor of the symmetry properties of them will be made, for adequate descriptions are available in many good books dealing with this specific subject. However, there is one important aspect concerning the arrangement of atoms in real crystals that now needs to be considered.

The unit cell of the metal chromium is shown in Figure 82. For this metal the Bravais lattice is body centred cubic, the lattice parameter is a = 288 pm and the motif is a single chromium atom located at the lattice points. The question now arises – is the array of atoms at every place in a crystal of chromium exactly the same as shown in Figure 82? Another way of asking the same question is – does the array of atoms in every unit cell of a crystal of chromium have the perfection shown in Figure 82? This same question can be asked for all crystalline materials and in every case the answer is 'no', for there are always present in real crystals of every kind some errors in the relationship between a few atoms or motifs and the associated lattice points. Although the frequency of occurrence is small, the errors are invariably present regardless of the kind of crystal, however carefully it has been prepared or however carefully it has been handled. These errors occur naturally and cannot be avoided.

CONCEPT No. 62.   ERRORS IN THE PERIODICITY OF THE ARRAY OF
                   ATOMS OCCUR IN ALL CRYSTALS.

An error in the relationship between a motif and the associated point of the space lattice produces a discontinuity in the array of atoms in the crystal. Such a

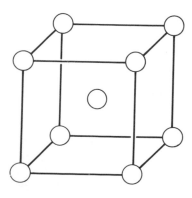

Figure 82. Diagram showing the body centred cubic unit cell of chromium with lattice parameter a = 288 pm

discontinuity is termed a DEFECT, sometimes a lattice defect but this term should be avoided since it erroneously implies that a defect exists in the array of points in the lattice and it has already been established that space lattices are always perfect. It is the periodicity of the array of (real) atoms that contains the defect.

DEFINITION No. 41. A DEFECT IN THE STRUCTURE OF A CRYSTAL IS ANY FEATURE THAT DISRUPTS THE PERIODICITY OF THE ARRAY OF ATOMS IN THAT CRYSTAL.

The defects that may occur can be classified as those features that:

occur at a point	: termed point defects,
occur along a line	: termed line defects,
occur over a surface	: termed planar defects, and
occur within a volume	: termed volume defects.

CONCEPT No. 63.   DEFECTS IN THE PERIODICITY OF THE ARRAY OF ATOMS IN A CRYSTAL MAY OCCUR AT A POINT, ALONG A LINE, OVER AN AREA, OR WITHIN A VOLUME.

While the nature of defects and the effects of them on properties and behaviour have been explored in detail in many other books it is proper to consider briefly the way in which the presence of the defects influences the periodicity of the array of atoms in a crystal and hence the three-dimensional pattern. This will be done by first considering point defects of which there are a number of different kinds. The three most common are shown in Figure 83 which, for simplicity, depicts only a single plane of atoms in some hypothetical crystal.

Figure 83(a) shows a part of this plane of atoms in which the array is perfect; a single atom motif is located precisely at each lattice point. The array is perfectly periodic in this region and as there are no defects there are no disruptions to the periodicity. Further, as there are some hundred or so different elements there are some hundred or so different kinds of atoms, each of which has a different size. Consequently, for the perfect array of atoms shown in Figure 83(a) to exist it is necessary that every atom have the same size and therefore that every atom be the same kind. This perfection certainly does not exist in the parts of the plane shown in (b), (c), and (d) of the diagram.

In (b) there is an atom missing from the array. As a result there is a lattice point V at which there is no (single atom) motif and the atoms surrounding this point are slightly displaced from the exact positions required by the periodicity of the array because of the imbalance created in the distribution of forces that holds the array together. The absence of the atom from its site is termed a VACANT ATOM SITE or simply a VACANCY. Sometimes the defect is called a vacant lattice point or vacant lattice site but these terms should be avoided since it is implied that all atoms in a structure are located at lattice points and, as is now known, this is not true for a structure in which the motif consists of more than one atom.

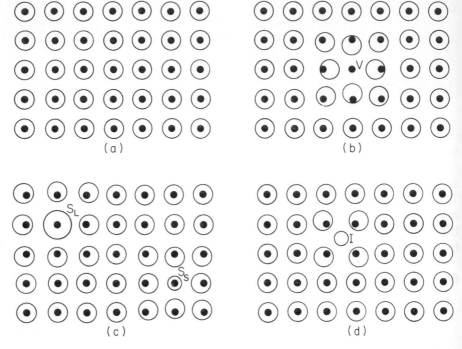

Figure 83. Four parts of a plane of atoms in a hypothetical structure having a single atom motif and showing in (a) a perfect part of the structure with one motif located in exactly the same way at each lattice point, (b) a vacant site, (c) substitutional 'foreign' atoms, and (d) an interstitial atom

DEFINITION No. 42. A VACANCY OR VACANT ATOM SITE IS A POINT-DEFECT IN WHICH THE PERIODICITY OF THE ARRAY OF ATOMS IN A CRYSTAL IS DISRUPTED BY THE ABSENCE OF AN ATOM FROM ITS SITE IN THE STRUCTURE.

It is also possible for two adjacent atom sites to be vacant as a DI-VACANCY and for three adjacent sites to be vacant as a TRI-VACANCY, and so on for larger groups.

In (c) the periodicity of the array of atoms is disturbed at two points by the presence of atoms having sizes different to that of the atoms that comprise the crystal. Let the crystal in (c), (and in (a), (b), and (d) of the Figure as well), consist of atoms of kind A so that the 'foreign' atoms having different sizes at S_L and S_S must be other kinds − a larger atom at S_L, and a smaller atom at S_S. Since the larger atom at S_L and the smaller atom at S_S have substituted for A atoms in the structure these 'foreign' atoms are called SUBSTITUTIONAL ATOMS and the defect is known as a SUBSTITUTIONAL DEFECT.

DEFINITION No. 43. A SUBSTITUTIONAL DEFECT IS A POINT DEFECT IN
WHICH THE PERIODICITY OF THE ARRAY OF ATOMS
IN A CRYSTAL IS DISRUPTED BY THE PRESENCE OF A
SUBSTITUTIONAL FOREIGN ATOM WHICH IS
NECESSARILY EITHER LARGER OR SMALLER THAN
THE OTHER ATOMS IN THE ARRAY.

It will be noted that the distribution of atoms around a substitutional defect is disturbed, the disturbance obviously being greater the greater the size difference between the two kinds of atom comprising the defect.

In (d) the periodicity of the array of atoms is disturbed by the presence of an additional atom located at a site which is between the atoms in the periodic array. The spaces between atoms in a crystal are termed INTERSTICES and it is in such interstices that additional atoms such as that at I can occur. These sites are called INTERSTITIAL SITES and an atom located at an interstitial site is called an INTERSTITIAL ATOM.

DEFINITION No. 44. AN INTERSTITIAL ATOM IS A POINT DEFECT IN
WHICH THE PERIODICITY OF THE ARRAY OF ATOMS
IN A CRYSTAL IS DISRUPTED BY THE PRESENCE OF
AN ATOM IN AN INTERSTITIAL SITE.

Additionally

DEFINITION No. 45. AN INTERSTITIAL SITE IS ANY SITE IN THE VOIDS
BETWEEN THE ATOMS IN THE PERIODIC ARRAY IN A
CRYSTAL.

Again it will be noted that the atoms in the array around the interstitial defect are displaced, the extent of the displacement depending obviously on the size difference between the interstitial atom and the interstitial site. Small groups of interstitials, termed DI-INTERSTITIALS and TRI-INTERSTITIALS etc., may exist, and further an interstitial atom of the kind that comprises the crystal may also exist and is termed a SELF INTERSTITIAL, but more usually it has a different identity altogether.

While the illustrations in Figure 83(b), (c) and (d) clearly show that point defects seriously disrupt the periodicity of the array of atoms in the immediate vicinity of them, the effect is highly localized and, provided that the frequency of occurrence is small, the overall effect is negligible and the periodicity of the array of atoms in the whole crystal is hardly compromised at all.

The concentration of vacancies in crystals rarely exceeds about 10^{-5}, that is one vacancy for every 100,000 atoms, but of course the frequency of occurrence of substitutional and interstitial foreign atoms must depend upon the purity of the crystal. Clearly, for very pure crystals (of elements) the total number of point defects is very small compared with the total number of atoms in the crystal and the three-dimensional pattern of the crystal, while not perfect, is nearly perfect with respect to these kinds of defects.

The geometry and nature of point defects in crystals composed of two or more kinds of atoms (e.g. sodium chloride) are somewhat more complex than in the simpler elemental crystals. Nevertheless the kinds of defect that occur are the same, the most usual being a pair of vacancies known as a SCHOTTKY DEFECT and the combination of a vacancy and an interstitial known as a FRENKEL DEFECT.

CONCEPT No. 64.   THE COMMON POINT DEFECTS THAT OCCUR IN
CRYSTALS OF ALL KINDS ARE THE VACANCY, THE
SUBSTITUTIONAL FOREIGN ATOM, AND THE INTER-
STITIAL ATOM.

Defects that have one dimension occur along a line, not necessarily straight, and are called line defects. The number of kinds of line defect is small but by far the most common is the DISLOCATION. No examination will be made here of the ways in which dislocations disrupt the periodicity of the arrays of atoms in crystals for this kind of defect has been treated more extensively in the literature than has any other kind of defect and adequate source material at all levels of understanding is readily available.

CONCEPT No. 65.   THE MOST COMMON DEFECT THAT DISRUPTS THE
PERIODICITY OF THE ARRAY OF ATOMS IN A
CRYSTAL ALONG A LINE IS THE DISLOCATION.

Two-dimensional defects occur over a plane, which is not necessarily flat and in fact generally has a complex curved shape. The most obvious kind of planar defect is the EXTERNAL SURFACE of a crystal for, as shown in Figure 84, the lattice points within a crystal are occupied by motifs (in this case single atoms), while those points outside the crystal are unoccupied. Clearly the periodicity of the array of atoms is completely disrupted at the free surface which thus constitutes a gross planar defect. A similar kind of planar defect, shown in Figure 85, is the GRAIN BOUNDARY of contact between two crystals (grains), in a polycrystal (see DEFINITION No. 23). The following features of the boundary should be noted.

1. The space lattice for each crystal, being infinite, necessarily extends into the other crystal.
2. The lattice points for each crystal are occupied by single atom motifs only within that crystal and so, for each of them, the boundary is the plane which separates the occupied sites from the unoccupied sites. In this respect the internal surface shown by the heavy line in the diagram is a gross planar defect, very similar to an external surface.
3. The positions of the atoms in the immediate vicinity of the boundary are compromise sites between the requirements for periodicity of the arrays of atoms in the two crystals in contact at the boundary. The exact locations of

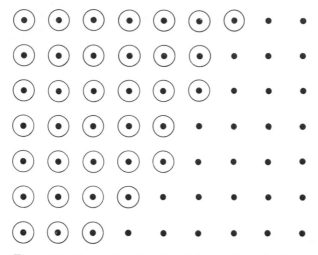

Figure 84. Part of a hypothetical structure having a single atom motif showing the defect associated with an external surface

these atoms depends on factors such as:

  (i) the relative orientations of the space lattices of the two crystals,
 (ii) the nature and strengths of the forces between the atoms, and
(iii) the sizes of the atoms, particularly if there is more than one kind of atom present in one or both of the crystals.

The actual structure of the boundary is not well understood for the detailed array of atoms that lie in and near it has long been a matter of great conjecture and controversy. However, it is well established that the complexity of a boundary is

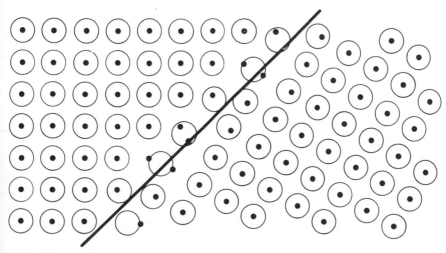

Figure 85. Parts of two adjacent grains in a hypothetical structure showing the defect associated with the boundary between the grains

144

greater than is suggested by the diagram in Figure 85, particularly in polycrystals containing more than one kind of atom, and when the orientations of the space lattices of the crystals on either side of the boundary differ considerably. Further, within all single crystal grains there inevitably exist small misorientations of structure producing other surfaces such as SUB-GRAIN BOUNDARIES, CELL WALLS, and MOSAIC WALLS.

It should be noted that the major internal surfaces are called grain boundaries only in polycrystals consisting of one kind of crystal. The boundaries which separate crystals of different kinds are properly termed INTERPHASE INTERFACES, each different kind of crystal being a separate phase of the material.

Additional to the internal and free external surfaces there are other types of planar defects, some of them flat, some not. These defects are the TWIN BOUNDARY, ANTIPHASE BOUNDARY or DOMAIN WALL, and STACKING FAULT (in close packed structures) but these will not be considered here for the two examples examined are the most common and adequately illustrate the way in which two-dimensional defects disrupt the pattern of the atoms in a crystal.

CONCEPT No. 66.   THE MOST COMMON KINDS OF DEFECT THAT DISRUPT THE PERIODICITY OF THE ARRAY OF ATOMS IN A CRYSTAL IN TWO DIMENSIONS ARE THE EXTERNAL SURFACE AND THE INTERNAL GRAIN BOUNDARY OR INTERPHASE INTERFACE.

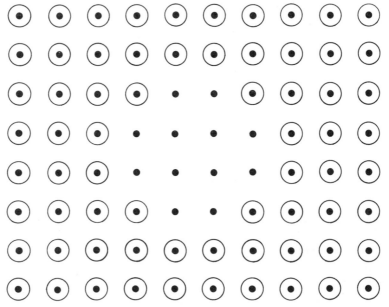

Figure 86. Part of a hypothetical structure showing the defect associated with an internal void

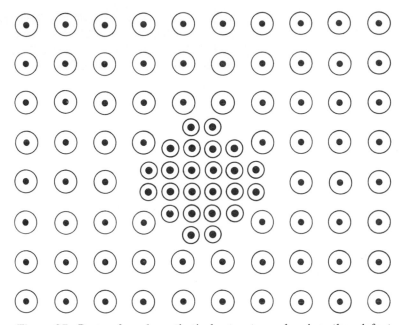

Figure 87. Part of a hypothetical structure showing the defect associated with a small included volume of a different structure

Finally, in three dimensions, the periodicity of the array may be disrupted by a volume defect. Obviously a VOID or HOLE in a crystal can be regarded as a collection of adjacent lattice points that are not occupied by the motifs of the structure and the periodicity is disrupted as shown in Figure 86. Similar defects occur as BUBBLES, CRACKS, and VACANCY CLUSTERS or VACANCY LOOPS. Alternatively, a crystal of one kind may contain, embedded within it, a small crystal of another kind. As shown in Figure 87 the presence of this small INCLUDED CRYSTAL disturbs the pattern of the surrounding crystal and a similar effect occurs in the presence of an INTERSTITIAL CLUSTER.

CONCEPT No. 67. THE PERIODICITY OF A CRYSTAL PATTERN MAY BE DISTURBED IN THREE DIMENSIONS BY THE PRESENCE OF SUCH FEATURES AS SMALL INCLUDED CRYSTALS OF ANOTHER KIND, OR SMALL VOIDS.

The few examples of defects shown in Figures 83—87 demonstrate that the array of atoms in a crystal may be disrupted at a point, along a line, over a plane, or within a volume. Defects are always present in crystals and it is emphasized that they are defects in the periodicity of the physical array of atoms arising from inevitable errors in the relationship between a few motifs and the associated lattice points. These defects are completely distinct from the space lattice which describes the scheme whereby the atom array is generated, and which, being a purely mathematical concept, is always infinite in extent and absolutely perfect.

Chapter 19

Miller Indices

Having now arrived at an understanding of the way in which the structure of a crystal is specified by the size and shape of the unit cell, the location within it of the various atoms of the motifs associated with the cell, and the nature and distribution of defects present, some of the other important properties of three-dimensional crystal patterns can be considered. These properties are similar to the properties examined earlier for two-dimensional patterns and arise from the periodicity of the array of atoms comprising the crystal.

The property to be examined in this chapter relates to the various planes and directions that occur in the patterns of all crystals. It will be remembered that in Chapter 6 the task of differentiating between the various directions and 'planes' in two-dimensional patterns was undertaken for quite unspecified reasons and that sets of INDICES were derived for this purpose.

It is now essential to appreciate why it is necessary that the distinction be made for the three-dimensional pattern of a crystal. Once this has been accomplished the procedures for finding distinctive indices for directions and for 'planes' in two-dimensional patterns will be extended to find distinctive indices for directions and for planes in three-dimensional patterns.

The necessity for distinguishing between various directions and various planes follows from the concepts of symmetry developed in Chapter 4.

DEFINITION No. 14. A symmetry element is any point, line or plane in a body about which an appropriate symmetry operation will transform the body to self coincidence

together with

DEFINITION No. 8. A symmetry operation is any operation that can be performed on a body to transform it to self coincidence

and

CONCEPT No. 18. Two or more positions of a body that are indistinguishable from one another are self coincident positions.

For any crystal, the existence of a symmetry element, other than the trivial elements of 1 and $\bar{1}$, means that within the crystal there are planes of atoms and/or rows of atoms which are interchangeable by the operation of the symmetry element. These interchangeable planes or rows of atoms are necessarily identical with one another. For example, in each of the crystal structures of caesium chloride (Figure 74(a)), sodium chloride (Figure 75), and chromium (Figure 82), the six planes of atoms comprising the faces of the cubic unit cells are identical and the twelve rows of atoms comprising the edges of the unit cells are identical, this being a consequence of the existence of the four 3-fold rotation axes of symmetry of the cubic system. It will be noted that the planes of the cell faces are different from other planes of atoms that occur in the structure and that the rows of the cell edges are different from other rows of atoms within the same structure.

Examine now Figure 88(a) showing the crystal structure of the metal silver which has a face centred cubic Bravais lattice with lattice parameter $\mathbf{a} = 408$ pm and

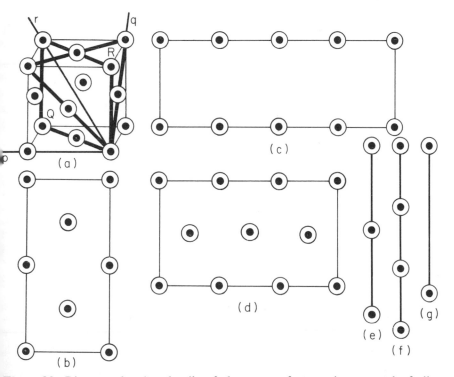

Figure 88. Diagram showing details of the array of atoms in a crystal of silver: (a) the face centred cubic unit cell with parameter $a = 408$ pm; (b) the array of atoms in any of the six equivalent face planes of the unit cell; (c) the array of atoms in any of the six equivalent planes of the type Q; (d) the array of atoms in any of the four equivalent planes of the type R; (e) the array of atoms along any of the three equivalent rows of the type p; (f) the array of atoms along any of the six equivalent rows of the type q; and (g) the array of atoms along any of the four equivalent rows of the type r

a single atom motif. Part (b) of the diagram shows the array of atoms in any of the six planes that comprise the faces of the cubic unit cell and which is clearly different from the array in any of the six identical diagonal planes of type Q shown in (c) or the array in any of the four identical diagonal planes of type R shown in (d), and so on. The idea is extremely important that, of the infinite number of different planes in a crystal (CONCEPT No. 42), many groups consist of identical arrays of atoms. Different planes in which the distribution of atoms is identical necessarily have the same d-spacing (from CONCEPT No. 43), and are called EQUIVALENT PLANES.

DEFINITION No. 46. TWO OR MORE SETS OF PLANES IN A CRYSTAL ARE EQUIVALENT IF EACH HAS THE SAME d-SPACING AND CONSISTS OF AN IDENTICAL ARRAY OF ATOMS. SUCH SETS OF PLANES ARE ALWAYS RELATED BY A SYMMETRY OPERATION.

It is necessary to identify the equivalent planes and to distinguish them from other planes for many reasons, but the following are sufficiently representative.

First, in the deformation of crystals, planes of atoms move relative to one another by a process called slip or alternatively by another process called twinning, the dominant process being related to the nature of the crystal. The movements occur more readily on some planes than on others depending among other things on the crystal system. To arrive at an understanding of the ways in which these deformation processes occur, it is necessary that the planes on which the movements take place be identified and so be distinguished from all other planes.

Secondly, the actual determination of the detailed array of atoms in any crystal is made using X-ray diffraction techniques in which the experimental measurements are interpreted by relating them to the various planes of atoms in the crystal. This procedure necessarily involves the identification of those planes using an appropriate nomenclature. The X-ray method of analysis will be explored briefly in Chapter 22.

Returning now to Figure 88, the parts (e), (f), and (g) show that the arrays of atoms along the rows p, q, and r are different from one another, but it will be noted from (a) that there are three rows the same as p (the cell edges), six rows the same as q (the face diagonals), and four rows the same as r (the body diagonals). These are only a few of the directions which exist in crystals, the total number being specified in CONCEPT No. 30.

CONCEPT No. 30.   A plane pattern and a plane lattice contain an infinite number of directions, all infinitely long.

Here a direction is as defined in DEFINITION No. 17. The same concept is equally true for crystals.

CONCEPT No. 68.　　A CRYSTAL AND THE ASSOCIATED SPACE LATTICE
CONTAINS AN INFINITE NUMBER OF DIRECTIONS.

Of this infinite number it is evident from Figure 88 that there are sets of directions which have an identical spacing between atoms or equivalently between lattice points. Different sets of directions with the same unit translation are called EQUIVALENT DIRECTIONS.

DEFINITION No. 47. TWO OR MORE SETS OF DIRECTIONS WITH THE SAME
UNIT TRANSLATION ARE EQUIVALENT AND ARE
RELATED BY A SYMMETRY OPERATION.

The necessity for distinguishing between equivalent and other directions is demonstrated by consideration of the physical and mechanical properties of single crystals (DEFINITION No. 22). The specific value of many of the properties depends on the distance between atoms in the direction in which the property is measured. Such properties necessarily have the same value in equivalent directions and usually different values in non-equivalent directions. A crystal for which the value of any property is direction-dependent is said to be ANISOTROPIC with respect to that property and the variation of the numerical value of any property of a crystal with direction of measurement is termed ANISOTROPY.

DEFINITION No. 48. A CRYSTAL IS ANISOTROPIC WITH RESPECT TO SOME
PROPERTY IF THE VALUE OF THAT PROPERTY IS
DIFFERENT IN DIFFERENT DIRECTIONS IN THE
CRYSTAL.

Note that a crystal is ISOTROPIC with respect to some property if the value of that property is the same in all directions.

It is not intended to consider further the various kinds of properties nor the anisotropy of crystalline materials, for this phenomenon has been mentioned only to demonstrate the importance of having available a system of nomenclature which distinguishes the directions in a crystal so that anisotropy, isotropy or other behaviour can be clearly identified.

It has been established now that crystals contain many sets of planes and many sets of directions — some of which are equivalent to others — and that for a particular crystal the incidence of equivalence must depend upon the total symmetry properties of that crystal.

CONCEPT No. 69.　　THE EXISTENCE OF EQUIVALENT PLANES AND OF
EQUIVALENT DIRECTIONS IN A CRYSTAL IS A
CONSEQUENCE OF THE SYMMETRY PROPERTIES OF
THAT CRYSTAL; THE NUMBER OF EQUIVALENT
PLANES AND DIRECTIONS IS HIGHER THE HIGHER
THE NUMBER OF SYMMETRY ELEMENTS IN THE
CRYSTAL.

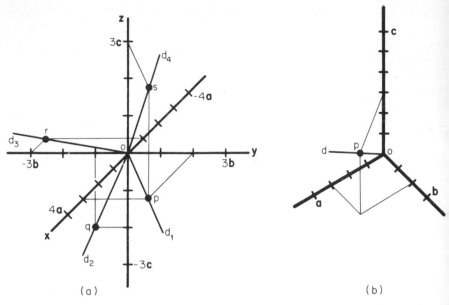

Figure 89. Diagrams showing: (a) the axes x, y, z of some structure, intersecting at the origin o and graduated in the unit translations a, b, c, with directions d_1, d_2, d_3 and d_4 on which are located the respective points p, q, r, and s; and (b) the axes of a structure for which a = 400 pm, b = 300 pm, and c = 600 pm, intersecting at the origin o and graduated in absolute units (100 pm) with a direction d containing the point p

It is also evident that a complete study of crystals and the properties of them requires a thorough understanding of the nomenclature which is used to distinguish between planes and between directions. For the purposes of achieving this understanding consider some arbitrary crystal for which Figure 89(a) shows the axes x, y, and z parallel to the edges of the unit cell with respective unit translations a, b, and c. Note that the axes, more correctly called CRYSTALLOGRAPHIC AXES, are graduated by the unit translations in both positive and negative senses from the origin o of intersection. The crystallographic axes are defined in a similar way to the definition of the axes of a plane lattice.

DEFINITION No. 18. The axes of a plane lattice are those two special lines parallel to the unit translations of the unit cell chosen to represent the lattice.

Thus

DEFINITION No. 49. THE CRYSTALLOGRAPHIC AXES OF A SPACE LATTICE ARE THE SPECIAL LINES PARALLEL TO THE UNIT TRANSLATIONS OF THE UNIT CELL.

The means of identifying the various planes and the various directions in this crystal are identical with the index system of nomenclature which was explained for the case of the two-dimensional pattern in Chapter 6. As applied to crystals, the nomenclature is derived from the *law of rational indices* developed in the mid-18th century by the French physicist and mineralogist Abbé René Just Haüy. The Welsh crystallographer William Hallowes Miller popularized the index notation of Haüy and consequently the indices which are now used to identify planes and directions are known as MILLER INDICES.

DEFINITION No. 50. THE MILLER INDICES OF A PLANE OR OF A DIRECTION IN A CRYSTAL OR IN A SPACE LATTICE IS THAT SET OF THREE NUMBERS ENCLOSED IN THE APPROPRIATE BRACKETS THAT IDENTIFIES THE PARTICULAR PLANE OR PARTICULAR DIRECTION AND DISTINGUISHES IT FROM ALL OTHERS.

The procedures for determining the Miller indices of any direction or of any plane in a crystal are exactly the same as specified in CONCEPT No. 31 and CONCEPT No. 32, respectfully, and these procedures will be now applied first to the directions d_1, d_2, d_3, d_4 shown in Figure 89(a) using CONCEPT No. 31.

CONCEPT No. 31. The indices of a direction are calculated by the procedure:
    (a) measure the coordinates of any point on the direction,
    (b) divide the coordinates by the appropriate unit translations,
    (c) rationalize the dividends,
    (d) place the rationalized dividends in square brackets.

First consider the direction d_1 and select on it the point p. The coordinates of this point are shown to be +3a on the x axis, +2b on the y axis, and zero on the z axis. Thus the coordinates are

    +3**a**, +2**b**, 0

Now, dividing by the unit translations **a**, **b**, and **c**:

    +3a/a, +2b/b, 0/c
    = +3, +2, 0

Since these dividends are integers the rationalization step is not necessary and the Miller indices of the direction d_1 are [320] — the three, two, zero direction — remembering that the square brackets denote a specific direction.

It is evident now that

DEFINITION No. 19. The indices of a direction are those integers in square brackets that identify that direction and distinguish it from all others

is equally applicable to directions in three-dimensional space lattices and crystals as to two-dimensional plane lattices and patterns.

For direction d_2 the point q is chosen and:

coordinates: $0, -1b, -2c$

divide by the unit translations: $0/a, -1b/b, -2c/c$
$$= 0, -1, -2$$

Rationalization is not necessary and the Miller indices of d_2 are $[0\bar{1}\bar{2}]$ – the zero, bar one, bar two direction – using the conventional notation to signify negative indices.

For the point r on the direction d_3:

coordinates: $-1a, -3b, 0$
divide by the unit translations: $-1a/a, -3b/b, 0/c$
$$= -1, -3, 0$$
and the direction is $[\bar{1}\bar{3}0]$.

Finally, for the direction d_4 and the point s:
coordinates: $+3a, +2b, +3c$
divide by the unit translations: $+3a/a, +2b/b, +3c/c$
$$= +3, +2, +3$$

and the direction is $[323]$.

The procedure which has been applied in an identical way to four different directions will, if similarly applied to any other direction, give the Miller indices of that direction. It will be remembered that the procedure can be applied if, and only if, the line of the direction passes through the origin of the axis system. However, as was pointed out previously, any particular line is a member of an infinite set of parallel, identical lines any one of which can be chosen for the determination of the Miller indices. Naturally, for any set, that one particular member passing through the origin of the axis system is the line used to make the calculation.

Now consider Figure 89(b) showing the three axes of a unit cell for which the unit translations are: $a = 400$ pm, $b = 300$ pm, and $c = 600$ pm. Note that in the diagram the axes are graduated in absolute units of measurement (100 pm), and not in multiples of the unit translations as was the case in Figure 89(a). For the direction d and the point p on it, the procedure used to determine the Miller indices is exactly as before:

coordinates: 300 pm on the x axis,
                        200 pm on the y axis, and
                        300 pm on the z axis,
                        i.e. 300 pm, 200 pm, 300 pm.

It is emphasized that in this case the axes are graduated in absolute units so that the coordinates are necessarily measured in those units, in this instance the picometre as shown. The next step is:

divide by the unit translations: 300 pm/a, 200 pm/b, 300 pm/c
                                    but **a** = 400 pm, **b** = 300 pm and
                                    c = 600 pm giving
                                    300 pm/400 pm,
                                    200 pm/300 pm,
                                    300 pm/600 pm,
                                    = 3/4, 2/3, 3/6
rationalize by multiplying by 12:   9, 8, 6.

Thus the direction **d** is the [986] direction and the same procedure applied to any other direction will give the Miller indices of that direction. For an arbitrary unit cell, some of the simple (low index) directions are shown in Figure 90. The origin of the axis system is the cell centre and the points where the directions emerge from the cell are clearly indicated.

It should be noted that the indices of any direction are quite independent of the actual geometry of the unit cell, being determined solely by the ratios of the coordinates of any point on the direction to the appropriate unit translations. Thus the angles between the unit translations are parameters which are irrelevant to the calculation. This has been asserted for plane lattices in CONCEPT No. 32 which, extended to three dimensions gives.

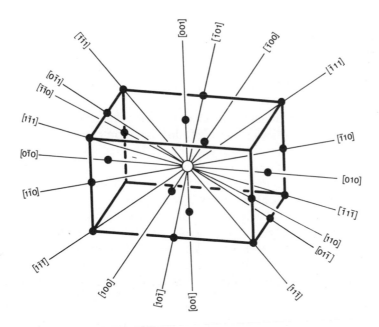

Figure 90. Diagram showing some important directions passing through the centre of an arbitrary unit cell; the points at which the directions emerge from the cell are indicated

CONCEPT No. 70.   THE INDICES OF DIRECTIONS IN A SPACE LATTICE
DO NOT DEPEND ON THE SIZE OR SHAPE OF THE
UNIT CELL AND CONSEQUENTLY SIMILAR
DIRECTIONS HAVE THE SAME INDICES IN ALL
LATTICES.

It will be noted that the selection of the centre of the unit cell as origin of the axis system in Figure 90 divides each line passing through it into two parts. The directions of these parts have identical indices except for reversal of the sign on each index. For example, the directions $[\bar{1}11]$ and $[1\bar{1}\bar{1}]$ are the opposite parts (senses) of the same line.

Sometimes it is required to refer to a general direction rather than to one with particular indices and

CONCEPT No. 33.   The general indices [uv] refer to any direction in a plane
pattern or lattice

extends in three-dimensional cases to

CONCEPT No. 71.   THE GENERAL INDICES [uvw] REFER TO ANY
DIRECTION IN A CRYSTAL OR SPACE LATTICE.

There is one other property of the directions in crystals or space lattices which needs examination, and this concerns the equivalence defined in DEFINITION No. 47.

Consider the unit cell for the cubic system. Since the unit translations $a = b = c$ the directions [100], $[\bar{1}00]$, [010], $[0\bar{1}0]$, [001] and $[00\bar{1}]$, being the cell edges, are equivalent, having the same unit translation a. These directions constitute a family.

There are in fact an infinite number of families of directions, each family being characterized by a particular value of the unit translation for every member direction. If it is required to refer to one of these families it is often inconvenient to list the Miller indices of every one of the member directions and so a shorthand notation is used. This notation utilizes the Miller indices of just one member direction but encloses them in angled brackets, i.e. ⟨ uvw ⟩ for a general family. This notation specifies all members of a particular family. For example (in the cubic system): the family ⟨ 100 ⟩ comprises the directions [100], $[\bar{1}00]$, [010], $[0\bar{1}0]$, [001], and $[00\bar{1}]$, and similarly the family ⟨ 111 ⟩ comprises the directions [111], $[\bar{1}11]$, $[1\bar{1}1]$, $[11\bar{1}]$, $[\bar{1}\bar{1}1]$, $[\bar{1}1\bar{1}]$, $[1\bar{1}\bar{1}]$, and $[\bar{1}\bar{1}\bar{1}]$, and so on. The unit translations for the low index directions in the three Bravais lattices of the cubic system are as follows.

FAMILY	UNIT TRANSLATION		
	P	I	F
$\langle 100 \rangle$	a	a	a
$\langle 110 \rangle$	$\sqrt{2}a$	$\sqrt{2}a$	$a/\sqrt{2}$
$\langle 111 \rangle$	$\sqrt{3}a$	$\sqrt{3}a/2$	$\sqrt{3}a$

For the cubic system the total number of members in the various kinds of family are as follows:

$\langle u00 \rangle$ (e.g. $\langle 100 \rangle$)	6 members
$\langle uu0 \rangle$ (e.g. $\langle 110 \rangle$)	12 members
$\langle uuu \rangle$ (e.g. $\langle 111 \rangle$)	8 members
$\langle uv0 \rangle$ (e.g. $\langle 120 \rangle$)	24 members
$\langle uuw \rangle$ (e.g. $\langle 112 \rangle$)	24 members
$\langle uvw \rangle$ (e.g. $\langle 123 \rangle$)	48 members

The detailed membership of the $\langle 100 \rangle$ and $\langle 111 \rangle$ families has been given but it would be most instructive to write out the full membership of examples of each of the other family types.

Consider now the $\langle 100 \rangle$ family of directions in the tetragonal system. Are there six members of the family as in the cubic system? If so, then these members must be $[100]$, $[\bar{1}00]$, $[010]$, $[0\bar{1}0]$, $[001]$, and $[00\bar{1}]$ and the unit translation for each direction necessarily must be the same. As should be appreciated, this is certainly not true for, in the tetragonal system, the parameters of the unit cell are a, a, and c. Thus, the unit translation for the $[100]$, $[\bar{1}00]$, $[010]$, and $[0\bar{1}0]$ directions is the same, being the parameter a, whereas the unit translation for the $[001]$ and $[00\bar{1}]$ directions is the parameter c.

Consequently, it is evident that there are only four members of the $\langle 100 \rangle$ family, the $[100]$, $[\bar{1}00]$, $[010]$, and $[0\bar{1}0]$ directions, the other two directions $[001]$ and $[00\bar{1}]$ being the members of the $\langle 001 \rangle$ family.

Similarly, the $\langle 110 \rangle$ family does not contain twelve members as it does in the cubic system but only four members – $[110]$, $[\bar{1}10]$, $[1\bar{1}0]$, and $[\bar{1}\bar{1}0]$, the other eight directions – $[101]$, $[\bar{1}01]$, $[10\bar{1}]$, $[\bar{1}0\bar{1}]$, $[011]$, $[0\bar{1}1]$, $[01\bar{1}]$ and $[0\bar{1}\bar{1}]$ – being members of the $\langle 101 \rangle$ family, or equivalently the $\langle 011 \rangle$ family.

All $\langle 111 \rangle$ directions have the same unit translation in the tetragonal system and so the family contains the same eight members as it does in the cubic system. The unit translations for the various low index families in the two Bravais lattices P and I of the tetragonal system are as follows.

FAMILY	UNIT TRANSLATION	
	P	I
⟨100⟩	a	a
⟨001⟩	c	c
⟨110⟩	$\sqrt{2}a$	$\sqrt{2}a$
⟨101⟩	$\sqrt{(a^2 + c^2)}$	$\sqrt{(a^2 + c^2)}$
⟨111⟩	$\sqrt{(2a^2 + c^2)}$	$\frac{1}{2}\sqrt{(2a^2 + c^2)}$

For the tetragonal system in general, the directions with indices composed of the numbers u, v, and w comprise the three families ⟨uvw⟩, ⟨uwv⟩, and ⟨wvu⟩ but note that in the family specification the first two indices are interchangeable because of the equality of the **a** and **b** unit translations of the unit cell. Thus the ⟨124⟩ and ⟨214⟩ is an identical family of directions and so on.

In the orthorhombic system the various low index families are:

⟨100⟩	comprising [100] and [$\bar{1}$00]
⟨010⟩	comprising [010] and [0$\bar{1}$0]
⟨001⟩	comprising [001] and [00$\bar{1}$]
⟨110⟩	comprising [110], [$\bar{1}$10], [1$\bar{1}$0], and [$\bar{1}\bar{1}$0]
⟨101⟩	comprising [101], [$\bar{1}$01], [10$\bar{1}$], and [$\bar{1}$0$\bar{1}$]
⟨011⟩	comprising [011], [0$\bar{1}$1], [01$\bar{1}$] and [0$\bar{1}\bar{1}$]
⟨111⟩	comprising the same eight members as for the cubic and tetragonal systems since each such direction has the same unit translation

The unit translations for each of these low index families in the four Bravais lattices of the orthorhombic system are as follows.

FAMILY	UNIT TRANSLATION			
	P	C	I	F
⟨100⟩	a	a	a	a
⟨010⟩	b	b	b	b
⟨001⟩	c	c	c	c
⟨110⟩	$\sqrt{(a^2 + b^2)}$	$\frac{1}{2}\sqrt{(a^2 + b^2)}$	$\sqrt{(a^2 + b^2)}$	$\frac{1}{2}\sqrt{(a^2 + b^2)}$
⟨101⟩	$\sqrt{(a^2 + c^2)}$	$\sqrt{(a^2 + c^2)}$	$\sqrt{(a^2 + c^2)}$	$\frac{1}{2}\sqrt{(a^2 + c^2)}$
⟨011⟩	$\sqrt{(b^2 + c^2)}$	$\sqrt{(b^2 + c^2)}$	$\sqrt{(b^2 + c^2)}$	$\frac{1}{2}\sqrt{(b^2 + c^2)}$
⟨111⟩	$\sqrt{(a^2 + b^2 + c^2)}$	$\sqrt{(a^2 + b^2 + c^2)}$	$\frac{1}{2}\sqrt{(a^2 + b^2 + c^2)}$	$\sqrt{(a^2 + b^2 + c^2)}$

In general, for the orthorhombic system, the set of directions with indices composed of the numbers u, v, and w consists of six families ⟨ uvw ⟩, ⟨ uwv ⟩, ⟨ vwu ⟩, ⟨ vuw ⟩, ⟨ wuv ⟩, and ⟨ wvu ⟩.

It should be clear by now that the lower the symmetry of a space lattice the larger is the number of families of directions simply because the number of equivalent directions in any lattice is directly related to the total symmetry properties available to generate them.

CONCEPT No. 72.   THE NOMENCLATURE ⟨ uvw ⟩ SPECIFIES A FAMILY OF DIRECTIONS ALL HAVING THE SAME UNIT TRANSLATION AND THEREFORE BEING EQUIVALENT; THE NUMBER OF SUCH FAMILIES IS DETERMINED BY THE SYMMETRY PROPERTIES OF THE LATTICE OR THE CRYSTAL.

Consider now the planes (as defined in DEFINITION No. 26) in a lattice or in a crystal and the procedure to determine the Miller indices as given in CONCEPT No. 34.

CONCEPT No. 34.   The indices of a plane are calculated by the procedure:
(a) measure the intercepts that the plane makes on the axes of the lattice,
(b) divide the intercepts by the appropriate unit translations;
(c) invert the dividends,
(d) rationalize the inverted dividends,
(e) place the rationalized numbers in round brackets.

This quite general procedure will be applied now to the planes shown in Figure 91(a), noting that the crystallographic axes x, y, and z, parallel to the edges of the unit cell, are graduated in the respective unit translations a, b, and c.

First consider the plane A for which the intercepts on the axes are infinity on the x axis, +4b on the y axis, and infinity on the z axis — remembering that a plane that is parallel to a line (axis) by definition, intersects that line at infinity. Thus for the plane A:

intercepts:	$\infty, +4b, \infty$
divide by the unit translations:	$\infty/a, +4b/b, \infty/c$
	$= \infty, +4, \infty$
invert:	$1/\infty, 1/4, 1/\infty$
	$= 0, 1/4, 0$ (since $1/\infty = 0$),
rationalize by multiplying by 4:	$0, 1, 0$

and the plane has the Miller indices (010) — the zero, one, zero plane — using the round brackets to denote a specific plane. Note that a plane parallel to A but on the

158

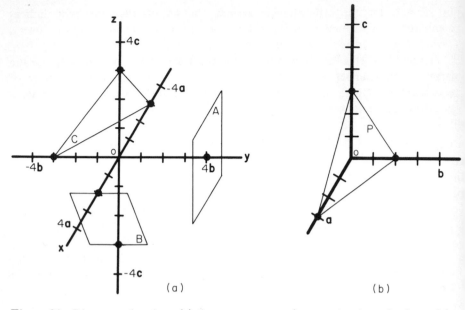

Figure 91. Diagrams showing: (a) the axes x, y, z of some structure, having origin o, graduated in the unit translations **a**, **b**, and **c**, and intersected by the planes A, B, and C; and (b) the axes of some structure with parameters a = 400 pm, b = 300 pm, and c = 600 pm, having origin o, graduated in absolute units (100 pm) and intersected by the plane P

other side of the origin has the indices $(0\bar{1}0)$ – the zero, bar one, zero plane.
 Obviously the

DEFINITION No. 20. The indices of a plane are those integers in round brackets
                   that identify that plane and distinguish it from all others

appropriately defines the Miller indices of planes in crystals and space lattices.
 The plane B is parallel to the y axis and so has:

intercepts: $+2a, \infty, -3c$

divide by the unit translations: $+2a/a, \infty/b, -3c/c$

                                     $= +2, \infty, -3$

invert: $1/2, 1/\infty, 1/-3$

                                     $= 1/2, 0, -1/3$

rationalize by multiplying by 6: $3, 0, -2$

and the plane is the $(30\bar{2})$ plane.
 Finally the plane C intersects all three axes:

intercepts: $-3a, -3b, +3c$

divide by the unit translations: $-3a/a, -3b/b, +3c/c$

$\qquad\qquad\qquad\qquad\qquad = -3, -3, +3$

invert: $1/-3, 1/-3, 1/3$

$\qquad\qquad\qquad\qquad\qquad = -1/3, -1/3, 1/3$

rationalize by multiplying by 3: $-1, -1, 1$

and the plane C is the $(\bar{1}\bar{1}1)$ plane.

If the axes are graduated in absolute units rather than in multiples of the unit translations the procedure for determining the Miller indices is unaltered but the intercepts must be measured in the absolute units of the graduation. Thus for the plane shown in Figure 91(b):

intercepts: 300 pm on the x axis,

$\qquad\qquad\qquad\qquad\qquad$ 200 pm on the y axis,

$\qquad\qquad\qquad\qquad\qquad$ 300 pm on the z axis,

$\qquad\qquad\qquad\qquad\qquad$ = 300 pm, 200 pm, 300 pm

divide by the unit translations: 300 pm/300 pm, 200 pm/400 pm,

$\qquad\qquad\qquad\qquad\qquad$ 300 pm/600 pm

$\qquad\qquad\qquad\qquad\qquad$ (since a = 300 pm, b = 400 pm and c = 600 pm)

$\qquad\qquad\qquad\qquad\qquad = 1, 1/2, 1/2$

invert: $1/1, 2/1, 2/1$

$\qquad\qquad\qquad\qquad\qquad = 1, 2, 2$

Rationalization is unnecessary in this case and the Miller indices of the plane are (122).

It will be appreciated by now that the Miller indices of the planes shown in Figure 91 (and of all other planes as well) depend only on the ratios of the intercepts to the unit translations and as a consequence the

CONCEPT No. 35.   The indices of 'planes' in a plane lattice do not depend on the size or shape of the unit cell and consequently similar 'planes' have the same indices in all lattices

can be extended to the three-dimensional case.

CONCEPT No. 73.   THE INDICES OF PLANES IN A SPACE LATTICE DO NOT DEPEND ON THE SIZE OR SHAPE OF THE UNIT CELL AND CONSEQUENTLY SIMILAR PLANES HAVE THE SAME INDICES IN ALL LATTICES.

Figure 92 shows some of the planes within the unit cell of some arbitrary space lattice. It is a worthwhile exercise to derive the indices designating each plane but

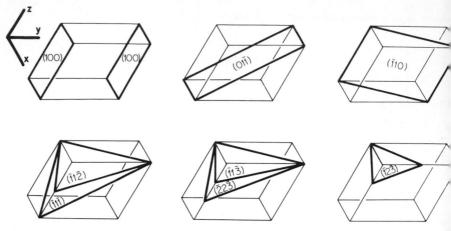

Figure 92. Diagrams showing some important planes in a unit cell of some arbitrary space lattice with crystallographic axes x, y, z

note that the origin of the axis system is not always located at the cell centre as in some cases it is more conveniently located at one of the cell corners.

Just as it is sometimes useful to refer to a general direction [uvw] in a lattice or crystal, it is also useful sometimes to refer to a general plane and for this purpose the index notation (hkl) is adopted. Thus:

CONCEPT No. 36. The general indices (hk) refer to any 'plane' in a plane lattice or pattern

extends to

CONCEPT No. 74. THE GENERAL INDICES (hkl) REFER TO ANY PLANE IN A CRYSTAL OR SPACE LATTICE.

Additionally, just as the directions in a crystal or space lattice can be grouped into families ⟨ uvw ⟩, so also can the infinity of sets of planes (hkl) be grouped into families. The member planes of each family are equivalent, having identical d-spacings and being composed of an identical array of atoms. Thus, each of the six planes (100), ($\bar{1}$00), (010), (0$\bar{1}$0), (001), and (00$\bar{1}$) bounding the unit cell of a crystal of the cubic system are identical and therefore are members of the same family. The shorthand notation used to identify a family of planes is a set of braces or 'curley' brackets. In this notation the {100} family consists of the six planes that are the bounding faces of the unit cell. Similarly the {110} family in the cubic system consists of the twelve planes (110), ($\bar{1}$10), (1$\bar{1}$0), ($\bar{1}\bar{1}$0), (101), ($\bar{1}$01), (10$\bar{1}$), ($\bar{1}$0$\bar{1}$), (011), (0$\bar{1}$1), (01$\bar{1}$), and (0$\bar{1}\bar{1}$). The complete list of the member planes of any family in the cubic system is the set of all combinations of the three indices so that the multiplicity of the various kinds of families of planes is exactly the same as the multiplicity for directions:

{h00}	(e.g. {100}):	6 members
{hh0}	(e.g. {110}):	12 members
{hhh}	(e.g. {111}):	8 members
{hk0}	(e.g. {120}):	24 members
{hhk}	(e.g. {221}):	24 members
{hkl}	(e.g. {123}):	48 members

For the non-cubic systems the multiplicity of most families of planes is less than the multiplicity of the same family in the cubic system because of the presence of fewer symmetry elements to generate equivalent planes.

For example, in the orthorhombic system:

the family {100} comprises two members — (100) and ($\bar{1}$00) d-spacing = **a**,

the family {010} comprises two members — (010) and (0$\bar{1}$0) d-spacing = **b**,

the family {001} comprises two members — (001) and (00$\bar{1}$) d-spacing = **c**.

Listing the membership of various families of planes in the non-cubic systems is a profitable exercise and should be attempted for a few representative cases such as {100} in the tetragonal system, {111} in the orthorhombic system, and so on.

It should be now appreciated that

CONCEPT No. 75. THE NOMENCLATURE {hkl} SPECIFIES A FAMILY OF PLANES ALL HAVING THE SAME d-SPACING AND ATOM CONFIGURATION AND THEREFORE BEING EQUIVALENT; THE NUMBER OF SUCH FAMILIES IS DETERMINED BY THE SYMMETRY PROPERTIES OF THE LATTICE OR THE CRYSTAL.

The one question which remains to be answered concerns the reasons for inverting the intercepts of a plane on the axes of a lattice in the procedure for determining the Miller indices. The necessity for the inversion operation lies in the identification of the actual feature that is assigned the indices.

In indexing the direction of a line it is the direction that is assigned the set of numbers that are the relative coordinates of some point on that direction. These relative coordinates, of course, are the Miller indices of the direction.

For planes, the most convenient parameters to measure are the intercepts that the plane makes on the axes but it is not the plane that is assigned the set of integers comprising the Miller indices. By convention, and for mathematical expediency that cannot be explained here, it is actually the line which is perpendicular to the plane that is indexed. The inversion step converts the measured intercepts of the plane on the axes to a set of coordinates for a point on the perpendicular to the plane. It is necessary to understand that these coordinates are not relative to the same axis system used for measuring the intercepts; the coordinates are relative to what are known as the reciprocal axes but to explain further would go beyond the scope of this book. The interested reader will find the

162

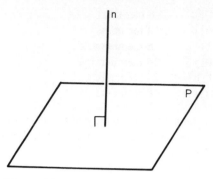

Figure 93. Diagram showing a plane P with normal n

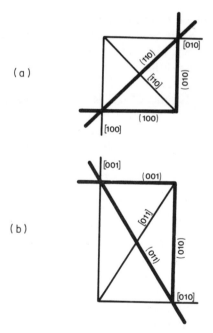

(a)

(b)

Figure 94. Diagram of a tetragonal unit cell showing: (a) the C face with the direction [100] perpendicular to the plane (100), [010] perpendicular to (010) and [110] perpendicular to (110); and (b) the A face with the direction [010] perpendicular to (010) but [011] not perpendicular to (011)

concept of the reciprocal lattice explained adequately in more advanced treatises on the subject.

Therefore, it should be evident that the inversion step is required to provide indices that identify the line perpendicular to the particular plane for which the intercepts are measured. This line is called the NORMAL to the plane.

DEFINITION No. 51. THE NORMAL TO A PLANE IS THAT LINE WHICH IS PERPENDICULAR TO THE PLANE.

Figure 93 shows a plane P with normal n.

For the purposes of many kinds of calculation and solving various kinds of problems in crystallography the normal to a plane is allocated a length which is the reciprocal of the d-spacing for that plane, i.e. the length of a line normal to a plane is $1/d$. It is significant that the interplanar spacing of a set of planes is most conveniently expressed as the length $1/d$ as will be seen in Chapter 21.

Finally, in general, the normal to a plane with indices (hkl) and the direction with the same indices [hkl] are not parallel but there are some exceptions to this generalization as follows.

1. For the cubic system, the normals to all planes (hkl) and the directions [hkl] are parallel, that is, the direction with indices [hkl] is identical with the normal to the plane (hkl) for all h, k, and l.
2. Certain directions in the tetragonal system are perpendicular to the plane with the same indices; viz. [100] is normal to (100), [010] is normal to (010), [001] is normal to (001), [110] is normal to (110), but [101] is NOT normal to (101) as shown in Figure 94.
3. In the orthorhombic system [100] is normal to (100), [010] is normal to (010), and [001] is normal to (001).
4. There are few other examples of a direction being normal to the plane having the same indices; for example the [001] direction is normal to the (001) plane in the hexagonal system, and the [010] direction is normal to the (010) plane in the monoclinic system, but such examples are exceptional.

Chapter 20

Miller–Bravais Indices

The classification of planes and of directions into families requires that:

(a) every member plane of a family has the same interplanar spacing **d** and is composed of an identical array of atoms; and

(b) every member direction of a family has the same unit translation.

Consequently:

(a) all planes having the same **d**-spacing and composed of an identical array of atoms must be members of the same family and so have equivalent indices; and

(b) all directions having the same unit translation must be members of the same family and so have equivalent indices.

These requirements are satisfied for the planes and directions in crystals of all systems except the hexagonal system.

Consider first the planes of this system and refer to Figure 95(a) which shows the hexagonal prism that clearly identifies the 6-fold rotational symmetry parallel to the c axis of the unit cell with parameters, a, a, c, and $\gamma = 120°$. Since the c axis of the cell is the 6-fold rotation axis, each of the six faces of the hexagonal prism must be equivalent and so must be members of the same family and have equivalent indices. Thus, it is necessary that the Miller indices of the faces F_1, F_2, and F_3 be equivalent. However, for the crystallographic axes a_1, a_2, c, the procedure described in CONCEPT No. 34 results in the Miller indices:

(100) for F_1,
(010) for F_2, and
$(1\bar{1}0)$ for F_3,

It is quite obvious that the indices for these planes (and others as well) contravene the condition that all equivalent planes must have equivalent indices. This difficulty arises from the existence of the 6-fold rotation axis peculiar to the hexagonal system and, for this system, necessitates the abandonment of the Miller index system of notation for the identification of planes (and of directions). Clearly some alternative system of notation must be used to provide equivalent indices for equivalent planes (and directions) in hexagonal crystals.

The preferred notation is based on a four axis system of reference as shown in Figure 95(b). These axes are the same as those used to identify the hexagonal unit

165

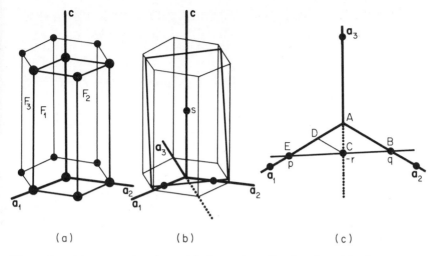

Figure 95. Diagrams showing: (a) the unit cell of a hexagonal structure together with some adjacent cells to identify the 6-fold rotational symmetry along the c axis such that the planes F_1, F_2, and F_3 are equivalent; (b) the four axis system of reference a_1, a_2, a_3, and c with some arbitrary plane that intersects the c axis at s; and (c) the intersections of the same arbitrary plane on the a_1, a_2, and a_3 axes at p, q, and −r respectively

cell, i.e. the axes a_1, a_2, c, together with an additional axis a_3 which is coplanar with a_1 and a_2 but at $120°$ to them. Thus there are three a axes labelled a_1, a_2, and a_3 at $120°$ to one another and all at right angles to the c axis which is the 6-fold axis of symmetry. Note that the a_1, a_2, a_3 axes are equivalent directions, being related by the 6-fold symmetry so that the unit translation on each of these axes is the same, i.e. a, and the indices of the axes must be equivalent.

Consider now some arbitrary plane that intersects the c axis at point s as shown in (b). The usual procedure (CONCEPT No. 34) used to determine the indices can now be applied to this plane relative to the four axis system as frame of reference.

As shown in the diagram (c) the intercepts of the plane are p on a_1, q on a_2, −r on a_3 (and s on c). Thus:

intercepts: p, q, −r, s

divide by the unit translations: p/a, q/a, −r/a, s/c

invert: a/p, a/q, −a/r, c/s

and these are the indices which can be represented by the general symbols (hkil).

Note that as intercepts on four axes are measured, the indices consist of four numbers the third of which, i, is the index on the additional axis a_3. The four index system of notation was adapted from the Miller index system by Auguste Bravais and is known as the MILLER−BRAVAIS index system of notation.

DEFINITION No. 52. THE MILLER–BRAVAIS INDICES IS A FOUR INDEX
SYSTEM OF NOTATION BASED ON FOUR AXES IN THE
HEXAGONAL SYSTEM.

From the derivation of the indices (hkil) of the plane shown in Figure 95(b):

$h = a/p$, thus $p = a/h$,

$k = a/q$, thus $q = a/k$,

$i = -a/r$, thus $r = -a/i$, and

$l = c/s$.

Since the axes a_1, a_2, and a_3 are related to one another by a rotation of $120°$ about the c axis, it is not surprising that the indices h, k, and i are related to one another. The relationship is found easily.

In the diagram in Figure 95(c) the triangle ACD is equilateral so that the length of the side AD = DC = r. Further, the triangles EAB and EDC are similar so that

$$\frac{DC}{DE} = \frac{AB}{AE}$$

and so

$$\frac{r}{p-r} = \frac{q}{p}$$

thus

$$r \times p = q(p - r)$$

or

$$rp = qp - qr \ .$$

Substituting now for p, q, and r produces

$$\left(\frac{-a}{i} \times \frac{a}{h}\right) = \left(\frac{a}{k} \times \frac{a}{h}\right) - \left(\frac{a}{k} \times \frac{-a}{i}\right)$$

so that

$$\frac{-1}{ih} = \frac{1}{hk} + \frac{1}{ki}$$

which, after multiplying by hki, and rearrangement, becomes

$$i = -(h + k)$$

or

$$h + k + i = 0$$

Thus, the indices h and k on the axes a_1 and a_2, respectively, determine the third index i on the axis a_3 simply as $-(h + k)$.

In the four index system, the faces of the hexagonal prism shown in Figure 95(a) have the indices

$(10\bar{1}0)$ for F_1,
$(01\bar{1}0)$ for F_2, and
$(\bar{1}100)$ for F_3,

which are equivalent as required for members of the same family.

Since the index $i = -(h + k)$, it is often omitted from the notation, being replaced in the Miller—Bravais indices by a dot (.). Thus the plane $(21\bar{3}1)$ in full notation can be written (21.1) with exactly the same meaning. Similarly the planes F_1, F_2, and F_3 are respectively (10.0), (01.0) and $(\bar{1}1.0)$ in the shorter notation.

The existence of the relationship $i = -(h + k)$ provides a very simple means of conversion from Miller indices to Miller—Bravais indices and from Miller—Bravais indices to Miller indices.

For example, some conversions are:

Miller indices	Miller—Bravais indices
(110)	$(11\bar{2}0)$ or (11.0)
$(1\bar{1}0)$	$(1\bar{1}00)$ or $(1\bar{1}.0)$
(345)	$(34\bar{7}5)$ or (34.5)
$(3\bar{4}5)$	$(3\bar{4}15)$ or $(3\bar{4}.5)$

and so on.

The problem for directions is similar, for as shown in Figure 96(a) the unit cell edges in the C plane of atoms in a hexagonal crystal have Miller indices of [100] and [010] with the face diagonal being [110]. However, it is clear that as the c axis is a 6-fold rotation axis these three directions are equivalent and as a consequence must have the same unit translation and therefore the same indices.

As for planes, the problem is overcome by using Miller—Bravais indices based on the four axis system a_1, a_2, a_3, and c. The procedure for determining the indices of some direction relative to the four axes is not as direct as the procedure in which

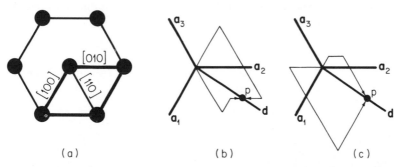

(a) (b) (c)

Figure 96. Diagrams showing in (a) the C face of a hexagonal structure with equivalent directions having different indices on the axis system a_1, a_2, and c, and in (b) and (c) four of the infinity of sets of coordinates of some point p on a direction d referred to the axis system a_1, a_2, a_3 (and c)

three axes are used as the frame of reference. The difficulty arises because the three axes a_1, a_2, and a_3 are coplanar and as a consequence a point p located on some direction such as **d** in Figure 96(b) does not have a unique set of coordinates on those axes. Four different sets of coordinates are shown in (b) and (c), and clearly there exist an infinity of sets of coordinates of the point p relative to the axes a_1, a_2, and a_3. Each set of coordinates results in a different set of indices calculated by the procedure described in CONCEPT No. 31 so that there is no unique Miller—Bravais indices for any direction.

Let one set of coordinates be:

m on a_1,

n on a_2,

q on a_3 and,

r on **c**.

The Miller—Bravais indices of the direction **d** for these coordinates are:

$$[uvtw] = \left[\frac{m}{a}, \frac{n}{a}, \frac{q}{a}, \frac{r}{c} \right]$$

As is evident, there is an infinite number of different solutions to this equation, but if the condition $u + v + t = 0$, that is $t = -(u + v)$, is imposed then:

(a) there is a unique solution for the indices of the direction, and
(b) most importantly, equivalent directions have equivalent indices.

The condition $u + v + t = 0$ is imposed on the indices solely to achieve these two consequences, and is obviously equivalent to the relationship $h + k + i = 0$ derived mathematically for the Miller—Bravais indices of planes.

The condition has the physical significance that it requires the coordinates producing the unique solution to be related by the equation $m + n + q = 0$ and consequently the relationship between the three numbers of the Miller indices and the four numbers of the Miller—Bravais indices is not as simple as it is for the case of planes. It will be remembered that for planes the conversion from one index notation to the other is carried out simply by the insertion or removal of the index $i = -(h + k)$.

For directions, the relationships that exist between the three Miller indices [UVW] and the four Miller—Bravais indices [uvtw] are:

$U = u - t$

$V = v - t$

$W = w$

$u = (2U - V)/3$

$v = (2V - U)/3$

$t = -(u + v)$ and

$w = W$

Using these relationships the Miller–Bravais indices of the three equivalent directions shown in Figure 96(a) can be found.

Direction $[100]$: $U = 1$, $V = 0$, $W = 0$

so that

$u = 2/3$

$v = -1/3$

$t = -1/3$

$w = 0$

and after rationalization by multiplying by 3 the indices are $[2\bar{1}\bar{1}0]$.

Direction $[010]$: $U = 0$, $V = 1$, $W = 0$

so that

$u = -1/3$

$v = 2/3$

$t = -1/3$

$w = 0$

and after rationalization the indices are $[\bar{1}2\bar{1}0]$.

Direction $[110]$: $U = 1$, $V = 1$, $W = 0$

so that

$u = 1/3$

$v = 1/3$

$t = -2/3$

$w = 0$

and the indices are $[11\bar{2}0]$.

It is evident that in the four index system of notation these three equivalent directions have equivalent indices and are members of the family $\langle 11\bar{2}0 \rangle$ or $\langle 11.0 \rangle$ (or $\langle 2\bar{1}.0 \rangle$ or $\bar{1}2.0 \rangle$) etc.

This same treatment can be applied to all planes and to all directions of the hexagonal system with the common result that the member planes of a family and the member directions of a family have equivalent indices. The hexagonal system is the only system for which this notation is necessary, the three index Miller system being satisfactory for the other six.

CONCEPT No. 76. THE MILLER–BRAVAIS INDEX SYSTEM OF NOMENCLATURE IS USED TO IDENTIFY PLANES AND DIRECTIONS IN THE HEXAGONAL SYSTEM TO ENSURE THAT EQUIVALENT PLANES HAVE EQUIVALENT INDICES AND THAT EQUIVALENT DIRECTIONS HAVE EQUIVALENT INDICES.

Chapter 21

The d-Spacing

So far in the examination of the properties of three-dimensional patterns and space lattices, the interplanar spacing **d** has been mentioned on numerous occasions. The interplanar spacing of equivalent planes must be identical, as too must be the atom array in them, and as has been noted also, the **d**-spacing is a measure of the length of the normal to a plane. Additionally, the **d**-spacing has many other important applications in crystallography as shall be seen.

In Chapter 7 it was established that, for a plane lattice, the parameter equivalent to the **d**-spacing is the separation s of lines in the lattice, and further, that this separation is related to the indices of the lines (treated as planes), and to the parameters of the unit cell:

CONCEPT No. 37. For each plane lattice there exists a particular relationship between the separation s of the sets of lines in the lattice, the indices of the lines (treated as planes), and the parameters of the unit cell.

A similar relationship exists between the **d**-spacings of the sets of planes in a space lattice, the Miller indices of the planes, and the geometry of the unit cell.

CONCEPT No. 77. FOR EACH SET OF PLANES IN A SPACE LATTICE THERE EXISTS A PARTICULAR RELATIONSHIP BETWEEN THE **d**-SPACING FOR THE SET, THE INDICES OF THE PLANES AND THE PARAMETERS OF THE UNIT CELL.

The procedure adopted in Chapter 7 of deriving the relationship for the general parallelogram unit cell and then finding the simpler relationships for the higher symmetry cases will not be followed for the three-dimensional case. The derivation of the relationship for the triclinic system is quite difficult and the detailed mathematical treatment would serve no useful purpose; similarly the derivation for the monoclinic, rhombohedral, and hexagonal lattices is complex and will not be given. For these four systems the results of the derivations are as follows.

TRICLINIC SYSTEM:

$$(1/d^2) = [h^2b^2c^2 \sin^2 \alpha + k^2a^2c^2 \sin^2 \beta + l^2a^2b^2 \sin^2 \gamma$$
$$+ 2kla^2bc(\cos \beta \cos \gamma - \cos \alpha)$$
$$+ 2hlab^2c(\cos \gamma \cos \alpha - \cos \beta)$$
$$+ 2hkabc^2(\cos \alpha \cos \beta - \cos \gamma)] /$$
$$[a^2b^2c^2(1 - \cos^2 \alpha - \cos^2 \beta - \cos^2 \gamma + 2 \cos \alpha \cos \beta \cos \gamma)]$$

MONOCLINIC SYSTEM: $(\alpha = \gamma = 90°)$

$$(1/d^2) = \frac{h^2}{a^2 \sin^2 \beta} + \frac{k^2}{b^2} + \frac{l^2}{c^2 \sin^2 \beta} - \frac{2hl \cos \beta}{ac \sin^2 \beta}$$

RHOMBOHEDRAL SYSTEM: $(a = b = c, \alpha = \beta = \gamma)$

$$(1/d^2) = \frac{(h^2 + k^2 + l^2) \sin^2 \alpha + 2(hk + kl + hl)(\cos^2 \alpha - \cos \alpha)}{a^2(1 - 3\cos^2 \alpha + 2\cos^3 \alpha)}$$

HEXAGONAL SYSTEM: $(a = b, \alpha = \beta = 90°, \gamma = 120°)$

$$(1/d^2) = \frac{4}{3} \frac{(h^2 + hk + k^2)}{a^2} + \frac{l^2}{c^2}$$

It will be noted that for these four systems at least one of the angles α, β or γ is not 90°. The three other systems — orthorhombic, tetragonal, and cubic — have the common property that $\alpha = \beta = \gamma = 90°$ and are termed ORTHOGONAL — three axes mutually perpendicular.

DEFINITION No. 53. ORTHOGONAL AXES ARE MUTUALLY PERPENDICULAR TO ONE ANOTHER.

The special set of three orthogonal axes with the same unit translation in the cubic system are ORTHONORMAL AXES.

DEFINITION No. 54. ORTHONORMAL AXES ARE MUTUALLY PERPENDICULAR TO ONE ANOTHER AND HAVE THE SAME UNIT TRANSLATION.

For the orthogonal systems the relationship specified in CONCEPT No. 77 is not difficult to determine and it is useful to see how the derivation is made in these rather simple cases.

Considering first of all the orthorhombic system for which the set of crystallographic axes are shown in Figure 97 together with some arbitrary plane which has intercepts of x, y, and z respectively on the axes. Note that the plane is located so that one member of the set passes exactly through the origin o and therefore the perpendicular distance from the origin to the plane shown is the

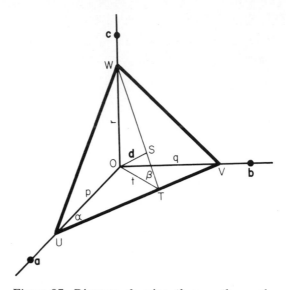

Figure 97. Diagram showing three orthogonal axes with unit translations **a**, **b**, and **c** and an arbitrary set of planes having spacing **d** and intercepts on the axes of p, q, and r respectively

interplanar spacing **d**. The standard procedure for finding the Miller indices of the plane can now be used:

intercepts: p, q, r

divide by the unit translations: p/**a**, q/**b**, r/**c**

invert: **a**/p, **b**/q, **c**/r

Thus, the Miller indices of the plane are (hkl) = (**a**/p, **b**/q, **c**/r), and so

$h = \mathbf{a}/p$, i.e. $p^2 = \mathbf{a}^2/h^2$

$k = \mathbf{b}/q$, i.e. $q^2 = \mathbf{b}^2/k^2$,   and

$l = \mathbf{c}/r$, i.e. $r^2 = \mathbf{c}^2/l^2$

Now in the diagram shown in Figure 97 the triangles OVU, OTU, OTW, and OTS are right angled triangles so that the theorem of Pythagoras and some simple trigonometry can be used to obtain:

$\sin \alpha = q/\sqrt{(p^2 + q^2)}$

$\sin \alpha = t/p$

$\sin \beta = r/\sqrt{(r^2 + t^2)}$,   and

$\sin \beta = d/t$

Squaring and equating to eliminate the angles α and β produces first, from the equations for $\sin \alpha$:

$$\frac{q^2}{p^2 + q^2} = \frac{t^2}{p^2}$$

from which

$$t^2 = \frac{p^2 q^2}{p^2 + q^2}$$

and secondly, from the equations for $\sin \beta$:

$$\frac{d^2}{t^2} = \frac{r^2}{r^2 + t^2}$$

Substituting for t^2:

$$\frac{d^2}{\left(\dfrac{p^2 q^2}{p^2 + q^2}\right)} = \frac{r^2}{r^2 + \left(\dfrac{p^2 q^2}{p^2 + q^2}\right)}$$

from which

$$d^2 = \frac{p^2 q^2 r^2}{(p^2 + q^2)\left[r^2 + \left(\dfrac{p^2 q^2}{p^2 + q^2}\right)\right]}$$

i.e.

$$d^2 = \frac{p^2 q^2 r^2}{q^2 r^2 + p^2 r^2 + p^2 q^2}$$

Invert to obtain

$$\frac{1}{d^2} = \frac{q^2 r^2 + p^2 r^2 + p^2 q^2}{p^2 q^2 r^2}$$

i.e.

$$\frac{1}{d^2} = \frac{1}{p^2} + \frac{1}{q^2} + \frac{1}{r^2}$$

Now since

$$p^2 = a^2/h^2$$
$$q^2 = b^2/k^2, \quad \text{and}$$
$$r^2 = c^2/l^2$$

the final solution is obtained for the

ORTHORHOMBIC SYSTEM:

$$\frac{1}{d^2} = \frac{h^2}{a^2} + \frac{k^2}{b^2} + \frac{l^2}{c^2}$$

In the tetragonal system $a = b$ so that for the

TETRAGONAL SYSTEM:

$$\frac{1}{d^2} = \frac{h^2 + k^2}{a^2} + \frac{l^2}{c^2}$$

Finally for the orthonormal cubic system $a = b = c$ so that for the

CUBIC SYSTEM:

$$\frac{1}{d^2} = \frac{h^2 + k^2 + l^2}{a^2}$$

This simplest equation, the equation for the cubic system, will now be explored in some detail to discover some of the more important features associated with the concept of the interplanar spacing.

First of all it is to be noted that since the Miller indices (hkl) of a plane are integers (i.e. whole numbers) the sum $h^2 + k^2 + l^2$ must be an integer also. Let this sum be the integer N. The question now arises — what are the permissible values of the integer N? Can N be 1? Can N be 2? Can N be 27?

For $N = 1$ it is required that $h^2 + k^2 + l^2 = 1$, the sum of the squares of three numbers is 1. What are those three numbers? The answer is obvious, one of the numbers is 1 and the other two are zero: $1^2 + 0^2 + 0^2 = 1$. For $N = 2$ two of the numbers must be 1 and the third zero: $1^2 + 1^2 + 0^2 = 2$, and for $N = 3$ each of h, k, and l must be 1. These very simple examples demonstrate the way in which the family of planes associated with a particular value of N can be found. To find the family it is required only to set up the equation

$$h^2 + k^2 + l^2 = N$$

and for the particular value of N find the three numbers h, k, and l which when squared sum to that integer. These numbers h, k, l are the indices for the family of planes for that N, i.e. the family is {hkl}. Note that for the cubic system $a = b = c$ and the indices h, k, and l are interchangeable for all planes. Consequently, for $N = 5$ the solutions $h = 1, k = 2, l = 0$, or $h = 1, k = 0, l = 2$, or $h = 2, k = 1, l = 0$, or $h = 2, k = 0, l = 1$, or $h = 0, k = 2, l = 1$, or $h = 0, k = 1, l = 2$ are all identical.

The solutions h, k, and l for the first few values of N are as follows.

N	hkl	N	hkl	N	hkl	N	hkl
1	100	11	311	21	421	31	
2	110	12	222	22	332	32	440
3	111	13	320	23		33	441 or
4	200	14	321	24	422		522
5	210	15		25	500 or	34	530
6	211	16	400		430	35	531
7		17	410	26	510	36	442 or
8	220	18	411 or	27	511 or		600
9	300 or		330		333	37	610
	221	19	331	28		38	611 or
10	310	20	420	29	520		532
				30	521	39	
						40	620

And so on *ad infinitum*.

Note that $N = 9$ specifies two families of planes, the {300} and the {221} families, both of which have the same d-spacing since for both $1/d^2 = 9/a^2$, i.e. $d = a/3$. However, it must be clearly understood that even though the {300} and {221} planes have the same d-spacings the two families of planes consist of entirely different arrays of atoms and for this reason are distinctly different as indicated by the different Miller indices. The same condition exists for the {411} and {330} families for both of which $N = 18$ and so $d = a/\sqrt{18}$, and for an infinite number of other families as well.

For $N = 7, 15, 23, 28, 31, 39 \ldots$ there is no solution to the equation $h^2 + k^2 + l^2 = N$, where h, k, l, and N are all integers, that is, there are no three integers which when squared sum to these particular values of N. These are 'forbidden numbers' N_F in that there is no family of planes in the cubic system that is associated with them. The complete set of numbers N_F is all the solutions to the equation

$$N_F = n^2(8m - 1)$$

where n and m are integers.

Thus for   n = 1, m = 1: $N_F = 7$
     n = 1, m = 2: $N_F = 15$
     n = 1, m = 3: $N_F = 23$
     n = 1, m = 4: $N_F = 31$
     n = 1, m = 5: $N_F = 39$
     n = 1, m = 6: $N_F = 47$ etc.,

and for $\quad$ n = 2, m = 1: N_F = 28

$\quad\quad\quad\quad$ n = 2, m = 2: N_F = 60

$\quad\quad\quad\quad$ n = 2, m = 3: N_F = 92 etc.,

and for $\quad$ n = 3, m = 1: N_F = 63

$\quad\quad\quad\quad$ n = 3, m = 2: N_F = 135 etc.,

and so on to generate the infinite set of solutions for the forbidden numbers N_F.

The smallest of the values of N for which there are solutions for h, k, and l are N = 1, N = 2, N = 3 and the families of planes {100}, {110} and {111} appropriate to these values have been considered in some detail. However, the next solution N = 4 specifies the family {200} which is a set of indices that seems to contravene the rationalization step in the procedure for determining the Miller indices of planes. This step requires that the indices be reduced to the set of smallest numbers in the required ratio. Thus the {200} indices seems to be an improper set which should reduce to the indices {100}.

It will be demonstrated now that, notwithstanding the procedure specified in CONCEPT No. 34 for the determination of the Miller indices of a plane, solutions such as {200} can, and indeed do exist, and have great significance. All that needs to be remembered is that the equation

$$\frac{1}{d^2} = \frac{h^2 + k^2 + l^2}{a^2}$$

specifies the relationship between the spacing d and the indices of planes in the cubic system. Examine now Figure 98 which shows the C faces of unit cells of three different hypothetical cubic structures having, for simplicity, the same lattice parameter a. In (a) the unit cell is primitive with a single atom motif and the planes of atoms indicated by heavy lines have d-spacing equal to the lattice parameter, i.e. $d = a$, from which:

$$\frac{1}{a^2} = \frac{h^2 + k^2 + l^2}{a^2}$$

The solution to this equation is $h^2 + k^2 + l^2 = 1$ so that the Miller indices are (100) and the planes are members of the {100} family as required by N = 1.

In (b) the structure is face centred cubic with a single atom motif so that the face centring atoms X are located at a distance $a/2$ below the plane of the atoms at the cell corners. Clearly the presence of the face centring atoms results in the presence of additional planes of atoms in the structure and the spacing of the planes indicated by heavy lines is $a/2$, i.e. $d = a/2$. Thus.

$$\frac{1}{(a/2)^2} = \frac{h^2 + k^2 + l^2}{a^2}$$

so that $h^2 + k^2 + l^2 = 4$, the Miller indices are (200), and the planes are members of the {200} family as required by N = 4. It will be appreciated that these planes are

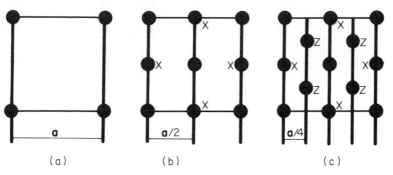

Figure 98. Diagrams of the C face of three hypothetical cubic unit cells showing: (a) planes with spacing **d** = **a** in a primitive cubic structure with one atom at each lattice point; (b) planes with spacing **d** = a/2 in a face centred cubic structure with one atom at each lattice point; and (c) planes with spacing **d** = a/4 in the face centred cubic structure of diamond

real planes, being composed of real atoms and so the identification of these planes of atoms by the indices {200} is as significant as the identification of other planes by the indices {100} (such as those shown in (a)).

The analysis can be taken a step further by considering the structure shown in Figure 98(c). This structure is also face centred cubic but the motif consists of a pair of atoms arranged in the way that carbon atoms occur in a crystal of diamond. In this structure, sometimes called the diamond cubic structure, the atoms X are located at the face centring sites (as in (b)) and the atoms Z are at the interstitial sites (see DEFINITION No. 45) having fractional coordinates:

1/4, 1/4, 1/4		3/4, 3/4, 3/4
1/4, 3/4, 3/4		1/4, 1/4, 3/4
3/4, 1/4, 3/4	or	1/4, 3/4, 1/4
3/4, 3/4, 1/4		3/4, 1/4, 1/4

Note that there are two alternative, but exactly equivalent, sets of interstitial sites that the atoms Z may occupy, the two sets being simply different ways of describing the same structure. The presence of the atoms Z has introduced additional planes of atoms and for the planes indicated in the diagram by heavy lines the **d**-spacing is a/4, i.e. **d** = a/4. For these planes

$$\frac{1}{(a/4)^2} = \frac{h^2 + k^2 + l^2}{a^2}$$

and $h^2 + k^2 + l^2 = 16$ so that the indices are (400) and the planes are members of the {400} family as required by $N = 16$.

Figure 99 shows the same three structures as shown in Figure 98 but with the emphasis placed on a different kind of plane. In (a) the spacing of the planes

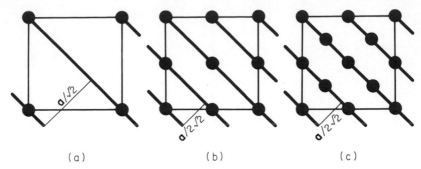

(a)   (b)   (c)

Figure 99. Diagrams of the C faces of the same three unit cells as shown in Figure 98 identifying: (a) planes with spacing $a/\sqrt{2}$ in the primitive structure, and (b) and (c) planes with spacing $a/2\sqrt{2}$ in the face centred cubic and diamond structures

indicated is $d = a/\sqrt{2}$ so that $h^2 + k^2 + l^2 = 2$ and the Miller indices are (110). In both (b) and (c) the presence of atoms at the X and Z type sites results in a different interplanar spacing $d = a/2\sqrt{2}$ so that {hkl} is {220}.

    These two examples are sufficient to establish that so called 'high order planes', viz. (200), (220), (246) etc., may in fact exist as real planes in some crystal structures. However, for many purposes it is not necessary that the planes be composed of an array of atoms for them to have significance. Some of the hypothetical planes which exist in all structures are shown in Figure 100 and, while having no physical substance, such planes have mathematical importance as will be seen in Chapter 22.

    One of the most important features of the d-spacings of the planes of a crystal relates to the dependence of the actual values of the spacings on the lattice parameters a, b, c, α, β, and γ, as specified in the equation for $1/d^2$ appropriate to each of the seven crystal systems. The lattice parameters for a very large number of crystals have been determined with considerable precision and, as far as is known, no two different crystals have identical unit cells. Thus, every crystal has a unique set of lattice parameters and, consequently, a unique set of d-spacings so that this set of spacings can be used as a characteristic which distinguishes each crystalline material from every other crystalline material.

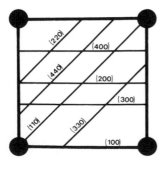

Figure 100. Diagram of the C face of a primitive cubic unit cell showing various real and hypothetical planes

As an example, consider the material caesium chloride with the primitive cubic structure shown in Figure 74(a). The lattice parameter a is 412 pm and the set of d-spacings for this material can be calculated from the equation for the cubic system:

$$\mathbf{d} = a/\sqrt{N}, \text{ where } N = h^2 + k^2 + l^2$$

Thus for $N = 1$, $\mathbf{d} = a/\sqrt{1} = 412/\sqrt{1} = 412$ pm;
$\quad\quad N = 2$, $\mathbf{d} = a/\sqrt{2} = 412/\sqrt{2} = 291$ pm;
$\quad\quad N = 3$, $\mathbf{d} = a/\sqrt{3} = 412/\sqrt{3} = 238$ pm;

following which for

$N = 4$, $\mathbf{d} = 206$ pm
$N = 5$, $\mathbf{d} = 184$ pm
$N = 6$, $\mathbf{d} = 168$ pm
$N = 8$, $\mathbf{d} = 146$ pm
$N = 9$, $\mathbf{d} = 137$ pm
$N = 10$, $\mathbf{d} = 130$ pm
$N = 11$, $\mathbf{d} = 124$ pm
$N = 12$, $\mathbf{d} = 119$ pm
$N = 13$, $\mathbf{d} = 114$ pm
$N = 14$, $\mathbf{d} = 110$ pm
$N = 16$, $\mathbf{d} = 103$ pm
$N = 17$, $\mathbf{d} = 100$ pm
$N = 18$, $\mathbf{d} = 97$ pm
$N = 19$, $\mathbf{d} = 95$ pm
$N = 20$, $\mathbf{d} = 92$ pm, etc.

Since no other (cubic) crystal has exactly the same lattice parameter as caesium chloride (i.e. a = 412 pm) no other crystalline material can have the set of d-spacings: 412 pm, 291 pm, 238 pm, 206 pm, 184 pm, 168 pm . . . *ad infinitum*. This set is unique to caesium chloride and so distinguishes it from other crystalline materials.

The importance of this property that every crystal has a unique set of d-spacings and that the d-spacings are related directly to the geometry of the lattice lies in the application of X-ray methods to the study of crystal structures which is the final subject for examination in this book.

Chapter 22

Crystals and X-rays

In the development of the concepts relating to the geometrical properties of three-dimensional space lattices and of three-dimensional patterns of atoms, a number of particular crystals have been examined in some detail to illustrate various aspects of crystal structure. The final question that needs answering is — how is it known that these crystals are composed of some particular arrays of atoms, or alternatively, how can the precise array of atoms in a crystal be discovered?

To answer this question it should be appreciated that to see the fine detail in any object it is necessary to move that object as close as possible to the eyes of the observer, but there is a limitation to this practice. Objects located closer to the eyes than the focal length (approximately 100 mm) cannot be focussed upon the retina to form an image without the assistance of some kind of artificial device. Such a device is inserted between the object and the eye to effectively move the object to within perhaps a fraction of a millimetre of it and so reveal the fine detail of the structure. The artificial device that makes accessible this fine detail is of course a microscope, which can range from a simple hand lens to a very complex light optical or electron optical piece of equipment. However, even with the aid of the very best microscopes the details of the structure of an object accessible to the most careful observer is still very limited.

Consider first of all the kind of microscope that is most familiar — the light optical microscope which uses ordinary visible light to illuminate the object and to form the image that is observed. Under normal circumstances the light is passed through a filter to produce a single colour and that colour is usually green for two reasons. First, the eyes are more sensitive to green light than to any other colour and so, when formed with green light, the image of an object is more distinct and can be observed for longer times with less strain. Secondly, the system of lenses in a light microscope is manufactured to operate most effectively in monochromatic (single colour) light and most efficiently when the light is green.

The important feature to emerge from these considerations is that the best conditions for examination of an object using a light microscope requires green light for illumination and image formation. As is well known, visible light comprises the colour band which is that part of the electromagnetic spectrum having wavelengths between 400 nm and 750 nm, with the wavelength of the green part being about 500 nm where 1 nm (nanometre) is 10^{-9} metre.

Now the image of an object formed with green light (or any other colour for that matter) can contain no more information about the object that is carried from it by that light. Further, the light, consisting of electromagnetic waves, can carry information about detail no smaller than approximately one-half the wavelength. Therefore, it is evident that green light produces an image in which detail smaller than 250 nm cannot be present. Even if blue light is used and the consequences of poor optical efficiency and poor eye sensitivity is suffered, the detail present in the image is only marginally improved. Thus, under the very best conditions an observer can hope only to see detail larger than about one-half the shortest wavelength of the visible spectrum, that is about 200 nm. Atoms are very much smaller than this and so some other kind of instrument must be used to determine the details of crystal structure.

Electron microscopes use electron waves for the formation of an image and since the electron wavelength is about 1 pm $(10^{-12}$ m$)$ it might be expected that high-energy electrons should be capable of imaging atoms which are between 100 pm and 300 pm in size. However, this is not so, for the optical system of an electron microscope is particularly inefficient and it is only with great care, using very specialized techniques, that this kind of instrument can be used to observe details of structure nearly, but not quite, as small as an atom.

Clearly then, if the array of atoms in a crystal is to be observed and measured, it is necessary to use a radiation which has a sufficiently small wavelength to carry information about the array, in conjunction with a technique which enables the information to be extracted to determine the identity and the location of the individual atoms in the structure. It has been noted that ordinary visible light is inadequate for this purpose, but it would be expected that the smaller the wavelength of electromagnetic radiation used to illuminate an object the greater would be the amount of detail to appear in the final image. Thus, to see atoms it would be necessary to utilize radiation with a wavelength of approximately 100 pm so that information about those atoms can be present in the image.

Radiation with this wavelength is X-RADIATION discovered by Wilhelm Roentgen in 1896. Later, in 1912 it was found that the internal order of a crystal indeed could be studied by irradiating that crystal with a beam of X-rays and analysing the scattered rays so produced. It is now known that the X-rays interact with the periodic array of atoms in the crystal to produce the scattered rays by diffraction and, since the scattered rays originate from a periodic array of atoms, the rays contain all the detailed information about the array. The only remaining problem is to discover how to collect and analyse the diffracted rays to extract the required information.

Unfortunately X-rays cannot be focussed by any known method so that the rays scattered by a crystal cannot be collected and used to form an image as the light rays scattered from an object in a light microscope are collected and focussed with glass lenses to form the image that is examined directly or photographed.

The impossibility of focussing X-rays with glass lenses (as in a light microscope) or with electromagnetic lenses (as in an electron microscope) to form images for observation or photography means that there is only one method available for forming an image from the scattered X-rays. This is the mathematical method in which the scattered X-rays are measured somehow and the measurements used to calculate the image which is actually that array of atoms that must exist in the crystal to produce those particular scattered rays.

In principle the experimental technique is very simple. A crystal of the material to be investigated is irradiated with a narrow beam of single wavelength (monochromatic) X-rays which enter the crystal, interact with the electrons of the periodic array of atoms comprising the structure, and so scatter to produce a few diffracted rays of very weak radiation. These diffracted rays emerge from the crystal and can be detected by photographic methods or with a Geiger counter or some similar device. The number of scattered rays may be increased by manipulation of the experimental technique and interested readers should refer to the Laue method, the rotating crystal method, and the powder method of X-ray diffraction in standard text books on the subject.

Figure 101(a) shows a beam of monochromatic X-radiation I incident upon a crystal C and a (weak) scattered ray S emerging from the crystal. The mathematical relationships between the geometry of the array of atoms in the crystal, the directions of the two beams and the wavelength λ of the X-rays were discovered originally by the German physicist Max von Laue and are known as the Laue conditions. A simpler, but exactly equivalent relationship, was subsequently developed by the English physicist Sir Lawrence Bragg inspired by his father Sir William Bragg and relies on the presence in the crystal of an infinite number of different sets of planes (CONCEPT No. 42). Thus, for any incident ray I and any scattered ray S there must always exist a set of planes such that the angle between those planes and the incident ray is exactly the same as the angle between those planes and the scattered ray. This angle, denoted as θ, is called the Bragg angle. The presence of such a set of planes, shown in Figure 101(b), provides a geometrical model of diffraction in which the scattered ray *appears* to have been reflected from those planes.

It must be emphasized that the X-rays are scattered by the physical process of diffraction, NOT reflection, but because of the geometry of the Bragg construction the scattered rays are quite often referred to, incorrectly, as 'reflected rays' or even 'reflections'. It is proper to call them diffracted rays or scattered rays.

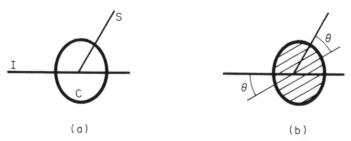

(a)   (b)

Figure 101. Diagrams showing: (a) a monochromatic beam of X-rays I incident on a crystal C and producing the diffracted ray S; and (b) the set of planes with spacing **d** which subtend equal angles θ with the incident ray I and the diffracted ray S

The relationship between the wavelength of the incident ray, and the **d**-spacing of the planes inclined at the Bragg angle θ to the incident and scattered rays is expressed in the BRAGG LAW

$n\lambda = 2\mathbf{d} \sin \theta$

where n is an integer $(1, 2, 3, 4, \ldots)$, known as the order of diffraction.

It is relatively easy to simplify the equation by eliminating from it all values of n other than $n = 1$. This will be now accomplished by referring to the cubic system for which it will be remembered that:

$$\frac{1}{\mathbf{d}^2} = \frac{h^2 + k^2 + l^2}{a^2}$$

Now, consider diffraction for which the appropriate plane in the Bragg geometry (Figure 101(b)) is the plane (100) which has a spacing d equal to the lattice parameter **a**.

Thus for

$n = 1:$ $\lambda = 2\mathbf{a} \sin \theta,$

and

$n = 2:$ $2\lambda = 2\mathbf{a} \sin \theta$

which, after rearrangement, becomes

$$\lambda = 2\frac{\mathbf{a}}{2} \sin \theta$$

Clearly this equation is appropriate to $n = 1$ and $\mathbf{d} = a/2$, the spacing of the (200) planes. For $n = 3$ the equation is

$3\lambda = 2\mathbf{a} \sin \theta$

which rearranges to

$$\lambda = \frac{2\mathbf{a}}{3} \sin \theta$$

the equation appropriate to $n = 1$ and $\mathbf{d} = a/3$ the spacing for the (300) planes.

These few examples establish that, for the simple case of {h00}-type planes in the cubic system, the integer n can be incorporated into the spacing parameter in the Bragg Law leaving the left-hand side of the equation as λ, and the integer n is effectively unity. This analysis can be extended to all planes in all systems so that the simplified form of the Bragg Law is:

$\lambda = 2\mathbf{d} \sin \theta$

Essentially all this means is that the nth order $(n = \text{n})$ diffracted ray for the {hkl} planes has the same Bragg angle θ as the first order $(n = 1)$ diffracted ray for the {nh, nk, nl} planes.

The usefulness of the Bragg Law lies in the application of it to the direct determination of the d-spacings for crystals by X-ray analysis. A crystal specimen is irradiated with X-rays having some known wavelength λ, the angles θ are measured for the various diffracted rays, and the associated values of **d** are obtained directly as

$$\mathbf{d} = \lambda/(2 \sin \theta)$$

It is most important to realize that the values of **d** are determined directly from the measured values of θ so that the accuracy of the calculated **d**-spacings depends on the accuracy of measurement of the angles θ.

It has been seen in Chapter 21 that the set of **d**-spacings for a crystal is characteristic of that crystal and so can be used as a means of identification. For this purpose a catalogue of the **d**-spacings of many thousands of crystals has been prepared and reference to this catalogue using established comparative procedures easily locates within it that set of **d**-spacings identical with the set found experimentally for some unknown crystal. That unknown crystal is thereby identified.

Of greater importance, perhaps, is the utilization of the measured Bragg angles θ for the calculation of the structure of the crystal from which the measurements were obtained.

It has been established that for each crystal system there is a relationship between the spacing **d**, the Miller indices of the scattering planes, and the size and shape of the unit cell, i.e.

$$1/\mathbf{d}^2 = \text{function } (h, k, l, \mathbf{a}, \mathbf{b}, \mathbf{c}, \alpha, \beta, \gamma)$$

It is always possible, at least in principle, to use this relationship to determine from the measured angles θ the h, k, and l appropriate to each associated value of **d** and so find the parameters **a**, **b**, **c**, α, β, and γ. The detailed procedures for making the determinations are to be found in standard reference books on the subject; only a brief summary of the principles involved in crystal structure analysis will be presented here.

The crystal properties to be identified in making a complete determination of the structure are:

(1) the crystal system;
(2) the lattice parameters;
(3) the Bravais lattice;
(4) the number and kinds of atom in the unit cell; and
(5) the locations of those atoms in the unit cell.

These properties will be now considered one at a time.

1. Determination of the crystal system

The crystal system is determined by a process of trial and error. The system is assumed to be cubic (for example) and the assumption then tested against the experimental data. If the assumption is found to account for those data then it may be concluded to be correct, and the system is thereby identified as cubic. If the assumption cannot provide a satisfactory account of the data then it is not tenable and the system is not cubic. The system is then assumed to be tetragonal (for example) and the procedure repeated. If the experimental data are not consistent with that assumption then further assumptions are made and tested until it can be shown that the data are consistent with the geometry of some particular system.

To understand how the experimental data are tested consider the cubic system for which

$$\frac{1}{d^2} = \frac{h^2 + k^2 + l^2}{a^2}$$

This equation is combined with the Bragg Law to eliminate the term d:

$$\lambda = 2d \sin \theta$$

i.e.

$$\lambda^2 = 4d^2 \sin^2 \theta$$

and

$$d^2 = \lambda^2/(4 \sin^2 \theta)$$

so that substitution results in

$$\sin^2 \theta = \frac{\lambda^2}{4a^2} (h^2 + k^2 + l^2)$$

Now, for some particular crystal with parameter a and an experiment using wavelength λ the term $\lambda^2/4a^2$ has a specific value; it is a constant. Let this constant be A. Further, the second part of the equation $(h^2 + k^2 + l^2)$ is known to be an integer identified previously as N. Thus, for a cubic crystal, the value of $\sin^2 \theta$ for each diffracted ray is the product of a constant and an integer

$$\sin^2 \theta = A \times N$$

It is evident that to apply this relationship it is necessary to obtain the set of $\sin^2 \theta$ values from the measured Bragg angles θ for the crystal. The crystal is assumed to be cubic and each of the $\sin^2 \theta$ values tested to determine whether it is the product of the constant A and some integer N which can have any value with the exception of the 'forbidden numbers' 7, 15, 23, 28, 32 ... etc. If it can be proven that each value of $\sin^2 \theta$ is equal to the product of A and N then the assumption is verified and the crystal has a cubic structure. The first few values of $\sin^2 \theta$ together with the appropriate values of A and N for three different cubic crystals illustrate the simplicity of the analysis.

(a) Caesium chloride (λ = 154 pm)

$\sin^2 \theta$	A	N	h	k	l
0.0349	0.0349	1	1	0	0
0.0698		2	1	1	0
0.1047		3	1	1	1
0.1396		4	2	0	0
0.1745		5	2	1	0
0.2094		6	2	1	1
0.2792		8	2	2	0

(b) Copper (λ = 154 pm)

$\sin^2 \theta$	A	N	h	k	l
0.1365	0.0455	3	1	1	1
0.1820		4	2	0	0
0.3640		8	2	2	0
0.5005		11	3	1	1
0.5460		12	2	2	2
0.7280		16	4	0	0
0.8645		19	3	3	1
0.9100		20	4	2	0

(c) Iron (λ = 71 pm)

$\sin^2 \theta$	A	N	h	k	l
0.0308	0.0154	2	1	1	0
0.0616		4	2	0	0
0.0924		6	2	1	1
0.1232		8	2	2	0
0.1540		10	3	1	0
0.1848		12	2	2	2
0.2156		14	3	2	1
0.2464		16	4	0	0

The relevance of the particular values of N to the determination of the Bravais lattice of the crystals will be demonstrated in the next section.

If it is not possible to account for every value of $\sin^2 \theta$ as the product of a constant and an integer then the assumption that the crystal is cubic is incorrect. The values of $\sin^2 \theta$ must then be tested for compatibility with the appropriate equations for other crystal systems. These equations in $\sin^2 \theta$ are obtained in exactly the same way as the equation for the cubic system by combining together the Bragg Law and the appropriate equation for $1/d^2$ to obtain the following results.

For the tetragonal system:

$$\sin^2 \theta = \frac{\lambda^2}{4a^2} (h^2 + k^2) + \frac{\lambda^2}{4c^2} l^2$$

i.e.

$$\sin^2 \theta = AN + BM$$

where the constant $A = \lambda^2/4a^2$

the constant $B = \lambda^2/4c^2$

the integer $N = (h^2 + k^2)$, and

the integer $M = l^2$

Note that the permissible values of N are as follows:

hk	N
10	1
11	2
20	4
21	5
22	8
30	9
31	10 etc.

And the permissible values of M are as follows:

l	M
1	1
2	4
3	9
4	16 etc.

To appreciate how the equation for the tetragonal system is applied, consider the tetragonal element tin for which the first two values of $\sin^2 \theta$ are 0.0700 and 0.0763.

It is easy to establish that tin is not cubic by showing that these two values do not satisfy the equation $\sin^2 \theta = A \times N$. For $\sin^2 \theta = 0.0700$ put $N = 1$, then $N = 2$, $N = 3$ etc. and so obtain the corresponding value of A. Each of these values of A is then used in turn to obtain a value for N (labelled N^*) from the second value of $\sin^2 \theta = 0.0763$.

$\sin^2\theta$	N	$A = 0.0700/N$	$N^* = 0.0763/A$
0.0700	1	0.0700	1.09
	2	0.0350	2.18
	3	0.0233	3.28
	4	0.0175	4.36 etc.

Since no value of N^* is an integer, the equation $\sin^2\theta = A \times N$ is not satisfied and tin does not have a cubic structure.

The second assumption, that the structure is tetragonal, is examined in the following tabulation for the first ten $\sin^2\theta$ values ($\lambda = 154$ pm).

$\sin^2\theta$	A	N	B	M	h	k	l
0.0700	0.0175	4			2	0	0
0.0763	0.0175	1	0.0588	1	1	0	1
0.1400	0.0175	8			2	2	0
0.1463	0.0175	5	0.0588	1	2	1	1
0.2163	0.0175	9	0.0588	1	3	0	1
0.2702	0.0175	2	0.0588	4	1	1	2
0.2800	0.0175	16			4	0	0
0.2863	0.0175	13	0.0588	1	3	2	1
0.3500	0.0175	20			4	2	0
0.3563	0.0175	17	0.0588	1	4	1	1

It is evident that $\sin^2\theta = AN + BN$, where N and M are the integers appropriate to the tetragonal system, and so the crystal system for tin is demonstrated to be tetragonal.

For the orthorhombic system:

$$\sin^2\theta = \frac{\lambda^2}{4a^2}h^2 + \frac{\lambda^2}{4b^2}k^2 + \frac{\lambda^2}{4c^2}l^2$$

i.e.

$$\sin^2\theta = AN + BM + CP$$

where the constant $A = \lambda^2/4a^2$

the constant $B = \lambda^2/4b^2$

the constant $C = \lambda^2/4c^2$

the integer $N = h^2$

the integer $M = k^2$

the integer $P = l^2$

and the permissible values of each of the integers $N, M,$ and P are 1, 4, 9, 16, etc.

For the heagonal system:

$$\sin^2 \theta = \frac{\lambda^2}{3a^2} (h^2 + hk + k^2) + \frac{\lambda^2}{4c^2} l^2$$

i.e.

$$\sin^2 \theta = AN + BM$$

where the constant $A = \lambda^2/3a^2$

the constant $B = \lambda^2/4c^2$

the integer $N = (h^2 + hk + k^2),$ and

the integer $M = l^2$

The permissible values for the constant N are as follows:

hk	N
10	1
11	3
20	4
21	7
30	9
22	12
31	13 etc.

While the permissible values for M are 1, 4, 9, 16 etc., as before.

The application of the equations in $\sin^2 \theta$ for the orthorhombic, hexagonal, and other systems is essentially similar to the application for the tetragonal system outlined previously for the case of the element tin.

The equations in $\sin^2 \theta$ for the other three crystal systems are quite complex and although not given here are obtained in the same way as described in detail for the cubic system.

It should be clear now that the determination of the crystal system for some particular crystal is made by simply finding the system for which the $\sin^2 \theta$ equation is consistent with the values of θ measured experimentally.

2. Determination of the lattice parameters

The lattice parameters are determined directly from the constants in the equation for $\sin^2 \theta$ that is compatible with the experimental measurements.

For example, if it is demonstrated that the measured values of $\sin^2 \theta$ are consistent with the equation

$$\sin^2 \theta = AN + BM + CP$$

then the crystal system is orthorhombic and the lattice parameters, **a**, **b**, and **c** are obtained from the constants A, B, and C evaluated in the process of correlating the experimental data with the equation. Thus:

$$\mathbf{a} = \lambda/2\sqrt{A}$$
$$\mathbf{b} = \lambda/2\sqrt{B}, \quad \text{and}$$
$$\mathbf{c} = \lambda/2\sqrt{C}$$

For the elemental metal γ-plutonium and X-radiation with $\lambda = 154$ pm it is found that:

$$A = 0.0594$$
$$B = 0.0178$$
$$C = 0.00574$$

so that the lattice parameters are:

$$\mathbf{a} = 154/2\sqrt{0.0594} = 316 \text{ pm}$$
$$\mathbf{b} = 154/2\sqrt{0.0178} = 577 \text{ pm}, \quad \text{and}$$
$$\mathbf{c} = 154/2\sqrt{0.00574} = 1016 \text{ pm}$$

In the simpler case of the cubic system the lattice parameter $\mathbf{a} = \lambda/2\sqrt{A}$ and using the information provided in section 1 the following values are obtained.

Material	A	λ	a
Caesium chloride	0.0349	154 pm	412 pm
Copper	0.0455	154 pm	361 pm
Iron	0.0145	71 pm	286 pm

The same kind of procedure is used for all other systems to obtain the numerical values of the lattice parameters.

It has now been seen that an analysis of the measured angles θ, i.e. the DIRECTIONS of the diffracted rays, provides the means of finding the size and shape of the unit cell. Alternatively, the geometry of the space lattice determines the directions in which the diffracted rays are produced so that the geometry can be determined from an analysis of those directions.

CONCEPT No. 78.   THE DIRECTIONS IN WHICH X-RAYS ARE DIFFRACTED BY A CRYSTAL ARE DETERMINED BY THE GEOMETRY OF THE SPACE LATTICE AND SO THE SIZE AND SHAPE OF THE UNIT CELL CAN BE FOUND FROM AN ANALYSIS OF THOSE DIRECTIONS.

3. Determination of the Bravais lattice

It has been established that the size and shape of the unit cell can be calculated from the measured directions of the diffracted rays but what is yet unknown about this cell is the location in it of the lattice points, i.e. whether it is base centred, body centred, face centred, or primitive. This information is obtained from a study not of the directions of the diffracted rays but of their intensities.

The Bragg Law specifies that diffraction of X-rays with wavelength λ can occur only for planes having a d-spacing greater than $\lambda/2$ since $\sin \theta$ has a maximum value of unity. Each such plane is associated with a diffracted ray which is necessarily less intense than the incident ray. The actual intensity of any particular diffracted ray depends on the detailed array of atoms in the unit cell and this in turn depends on the location in the cell of the motifs of the structure and thus the location of the lattice points.

Some rays have zero intensity and it is from considerations of these 'absent rays' that the type of Bravais lattice is determined. The factors that influence the intensity of the diffracted rays will not be considered here but the analyses in standard text books show that the following conditions prevail.

(a) If the Bravais lattice is body centred I those planes (hkl) for which h + k + l is an odd number (i.e. $h^2 + k^2 + l^2 = N$ is an odd number) produce diffracted rays with zero intensity. Thus, if the only diffracted rays to emerge from the crystal are those associated with planes for which N is an even number, then the Bravais lattice of that crystal is body centred I.

(b) If the Bravais lattice is face centred F those planes for which the indices h, k, and l are mixed odd and even numbers (with zero considered to be an even number) produce diffracted rays with zero intensity. Thus, if the only diffracted rays to emerge from a crystal are those associated with planes having unmixed indices (i.e. for each plane the three indices are either all even or all odd) then the Bravais lattice of the crystal is face centred F.

(c) If the Bravais lattice is base centred then one of the three conditions h + k, or h + l, or k + l be an even number must prevail. If the only diffracted rays to emerge from a crystal satisfy h + k = an even number, then the space lattice of the crystal is C base centred; if h + l = an even number then the lattice is B base centred, and if k + l = an even number the lattice is A base centred. Note that if all three conditions are satisfied then h, k, and l must be all even or be all odd and the Bravais lattice is face centred, being centred on each of the A, B, and C faces.

(d) If none of the systematic absences described in (a), (b), or (c) occur then the Bravais lattice is not body centred, not face centred, not base centred and so by elimination the lattice must be primitive P. It is emphasized that the only way to prove that a Bravais lattice is primitive is to eliminate the other three possibilities.

Referring back to section 1 in which the $\sin^2 \theta$ and associated values of N were listed for three cubic crystals it is evident that the Bravais lattices are primitive P for caesium chloride, face centred F for copper, and body centred I for iron.

4. Determination of the number and kinds of atoms in the unit cell

It has been established that the size and shape of the unit cell is specified by the directions of the diffracted rays to emerge from a crystal and the systematic absences from those diffracted rays identify the type of Bravais lattice — that is, the location in the unit cell of the lattice points.

The next step in the determination of the structure is to discover the numbers of the various kinds of atoms that are located within the unit cell. To obtain this information a chemical analysis of the material of the crystal or knowledge of the composition of it together with an approximate value of the density is needed.

Consider a material with composition A_2B_3C, that is, a material composed of atoms of kinds A, B, and C in the ratio $2 : 3 : 1$ and with density ρ kilogram per cubic metre (kg m^{-3}).

Now, since density = mass per unit volume

$$= \text{mass/volume}$$

$$\text{density} = \frac{\text{mass of the atoms in the unit cell}}{\text{volume of the unit cell}}$$

The mass of the atoms in the unit cell is the number n of groups of A_2B_3C in the cell multiplied by the mass m of each group. Thus

$$\text{density} = \frac{n \times m}{\text{volume of unit cell}}$$

Note that the number n must be an integer since the array of atoms in each motif is identical, there is one motif at each lattice point, and an integral number of lattice points in the cell. The mass m of each group is obtained from the equation

$$L\,m = M$$

where L is the Avogadro constant (6.023×10^{23} mol^{-1}) and M is the molar mass (note that the mole is the standard unit of amount of a substance). The molar mass M is obtained from the molecular weight M_W as

$$M = M_W \times 10^{-3} \text{ kg mol}^{-1}$$

and the molecular weight of A_2B_3C is simply

$$M_W = (2 \times A_A) + (3 \times A_B) + (1 \times A_C)$$

where A_A A_B and A_C are the atomic weights of the respective elements A, B, and C.

Thus, for this material:

$$\rho = \frac{n[(2 \times A_A) + (3 \times A_B) + (1 \times A_C)] \times 10^{-3}}{L \times \text{volume of the unit cell}}$$

Since L and the atomic weights of the elements are known with considerable precision, and the volume of the unit cell can be calculated accurately from the measured lattice parameters, an approximate value of n can be obtained from the approximate value of the density. However, and the number n must be an integer, the correct value of n is that integer closest to the approximate value obtained from the calculation.

Note that as there is only one, two, or four lattice points in a unit cell and the number of atom groups associated with each must be identical, then the integer n must be a multiple of 1, 2, or 4. For a primitive Bravais lattice n can be any integer, for a body centred or a base centred lattice n must be a multiple of 2, and for a face centred lattice n must be a multiple of 4.

It is also worth noting that once the integer n has been found it is possible to work back through the equation to obtain a precise value of the density and in fact it is by this method that high precision values of density are determined.

The application of the method will be illustrated now by calculating the number of molecules of ZnS in the unit cell of the mineral zinc blende (sphalerite) which has a face centred cubic structure with lattice parameter a = 540.6 pm (= 540.6 x 10^{-12} m), and approximate density of 4000 kg m^{-3}. Thus

$$\text{density} = \frac{n \times (A_{Zn} + A_S) \times 10^{-3}}{L \times a^3}$$

$$4000 = \frac{n(65.4 + 32.1) \times 10^{-3}}{6.023 \times 10^{23} \times (540.6 \times 10^{-12})^3}$$

from which n = 3.90 and therefore there must be four molecules in the unit cell since 4 is the integer closest to 3.90. Further, as the Bravais lattice is face centred, the unit cell contains four lattice points and there must be one molecule of ZnS associated with each point. Note that the reverse calculation using n = 4 shows that the correct density of the mineral is 4103 kg m^{-3}.

5. Determination of the atom sites in the unit cell

Sections 1–4 describe the ways by which X-ray diffraction data can be used to find the crystal system, the lattice parameters, the location in the unit cell of the lattice points and the number of each kind of atom in the unit cell of some crystalline material. All that remains to complete the determination of the crystal structure is to specify, by the appropriate fractional coordinates, the location of the various atoms in the cell.

The principle involved in this final part of the crystal structure analysis is simply that the distribution of atoms in the cell determines the intensities of the diffracted rays. More correctly, it is the distribution of electrons in the unit cell that determines the intensities, but, since the electron density is high at the site of an atom, the distribution of electron density and the distribution of atoms is the same. Thus, each diffracted ray is the sum of the contributions from all atoms in the cell, and the contributions depend on the locations and identities (number of associated electrons) of those atoms. It has already been seen that an analysis of the planes associated with the rays having zero intensity leads to the determination of the Bravais lattice specifying the distribution of motifs in the unit cell. The other rays, having non-zero intensity, vary from very weak to very strong and the intensities of these rays can be measured with considerable precision either relative to one another or absolutely, relative to the incident ray. These measured intensities can be analysed with a variety of mathematical procedures to obtain the fractional coordinates of each of the atoms within the cell.

This analysis is far from easy for crystals which contain more than a few atoms in the motif, and is so exceptionally difficult for crystals with many atoms in the motif that even the barest details of the procedures involved are well beyond the scope of this book. Nevertheless, the results obtained from the mathematical analyses are the fractional coordinates and identity of each of the atoms in the unit cell that most nearly agree with the intensity measurements.

CONCEPT No. 79.   THE INTENSITIES OF THE X-RAYS WHICH ARE DIFFRACTED BY A CRYSTAL ARE DETERMINED BY THE DISTRIBUTION OF ELECTRONS IN THAT CRYSTAL AND SO THE LOCATION AND IDENTITY OF EACH ATOM IN THE UNIT CELL CAN BE FOUND FROM AN ANALYSIS OF THE INTENSITIES.

These brief considerations of the phenomenon of X-ray diffraction demonstrate that the directions of the diffracted beams are determined by the size and shape of the unit cell and the intensities of the diffracted beams are determined by the locations in the unit cell of the motifs and various atoms in the motifs. It is from these basic principles that the structures of crystals and the various details of structure described in this book and elsewhere for many thousands of crystalline materials have been determined.

Index

A number in *italics* indicates the page where the index entry is defined

ANISOTROPY, *149*
ATOM SITES, DETERMINATION OF, 193
AXES OF PLANE LATTICE, 48
AXES, CRYSTALLOGRAPHIC, *150*
   ORTHOGONAL, *171*
   ORTHONORMAL, *171*
AXIS, *28*, 75

BASE CENTRED CELL, *99*
BODY CENTRED CELL, *100*
BRAGG LAW, 183
BRAVAIS LATTICES, 97f, *107*
   BASE CENTRED, *99*
   BODY CENTRED, *100*
   DETERMINATION OF, 191
   FACE CENTRED, *102*
   PRIMITIVE, 102

CENTRE OF SYMMETRY, *38*, 78
CENTRED UNIT CELL, 26, 98
   BASE, *99*
   BODY, *100*
   FACE, *102*
COORDINATES, *43*, 118
   FRACTIONAL, 41f, *43*, 118f
CRYSTAL, 61f, *62*
   SINGLE, *62*
CRYSTAL CLASS, 83
   STRUCTURE, *67*, 118f
   SYSTEM, 88f, *89*
      CUBIC, 89, 90
      DETERMINATION OF, 184f
      HEXAGONAL, 89, 90
      MONOCLINIC, 89
      ORTHORHOMBIC, 89, 90
      RHOMBOHEDRAL, 89, 90
      TETRAGONAL, 89, 90
      TRICLINIC, 89

CRYSTALLOGRAPHIC AXES, *150*
CUBIC SYSTEM, 89
   UNIT CELL, 90

d-SPACING, *70*, 170f
DEFECTS IN CRYSTALS, 138f, *139*
   LINE, 142
   PLANAR, 142
   POINT, 139
   VOLUME, 145
DIRECTIONS, *46*
   EQUIVALENT, *149*
   FAMILY OF, 154
DISLOCATION, 142

EQUIVALENT DIRECTIONS, *149*
   PLANES, *148*

FACE CENTRED CELL, *102*
FAMILY OF DIRECTIONS, 154
   PLANES, 160
FRACTIONAL COORDINATES, 41f, *43*, 118f

GLIDE PLANE, *130*
GRAIN, 62
   BOUNDARY, 142

HEXAGONAL SYSTEM, 89
   UNIT CELL, 90

INDICES, IN PLANE LATTICES, 46f
   OF DIRECTIONS, 48, *49*, 151f, 167
   OF PLANES, 52, *54*, 157f, 164
INDICES, MILLER, 146f, *151*
   MILLER–BRAVAIS, 164f, *166*
INTERCEPTS, 52
INTERSTICE, 141

INTERSTITIAL DEFECT, *141*
  SITE, *141*
INVERSION, 37, 78
ISOTROPY, 149

LATTICE, PLANE, 10f, *12*
  SPACE, 66f, *66*
LATTICE PARAMETERS, *20*, 73
    DETERMINATION OF, 189
  POINT, *12*, 66
    NUMBER PER UNIT CELL, 21, 93, 102
LINE DEFECT, 142
  SPACING s, 14, 57f

MACROSCOPIC SYMMETRY, 75f
  ELEMENTS, *82*
    CENTRE, *38*, 78
    MIRROR PLANE, *34*, 78
    ROTARY INVERSION AXIS, *79*
    ROTATION AXIS, *28*, *29*, 75
MICROSCOPIC SYMMETRY, 129f
  ELEMENTS, *133*
    GLIDE PLANE, *130*
    SCREW AXIS, *131*
MILLER INDICES, 146f, *151*
  OF DIRECTIONS, 151f
  OF PLANES, 157f
MILLER–BRAVAIS INDICES, 164f, *166*
  OF DIRECTIONS, 167
  OF PLANES, 164
MIRROR PLANE, *34*, 78
MONOCLINIC SYSTEM, 89
  UNIT CELL, 89
MOTIF, 1
  OF CRYSTAL STRUCTURE, 63

N-FOLD ROTATION AXIS, *29*
NON-PRIMITIVE UNIT CELL, *23*, 94
NORMAL TO PLANE, *163*

ORTHOGONAL AXES, *171*
ORTHONORMAL AXES, *171*
ORTHORHOMBIC SYSTEM, 89
  UNIT CELL, 90

PATTERNS, 1f
PLANAR DEFECT, 142
PLANE LATTICE, 10f, *12*
  UNIT CELL OF, 17f, *17*
  PATTERN, 1f
PLANES, 47, *67*
  d-SPACING, *70*, 170f

EQUIVALENT, *148*
FAMILY OF, 160
NORMAL TO, *163*
POINT DEFECT, 139
GROUPS, 83f, *83*
POLYCRYSTAL, *62*
PRIMITIVE UNIT CELL, *22*, 94

REFLECTION, 34, 78
RHOMBOHEDRAL SYSTEM, 89
  UNIT CELL, 90
ROTARY INVERSION, 79
  AXIS, *79*
ROTATION AXIS, *28*, 75
  N-FOLD, *29*, 75
ROTATIONAL SYMMETRY, 27f, 75f

SCHEME OF REPETITION, 1, 67
SCREW AXIS, *131*
SELECTION OF UNIT CELL:
  IN PLANE LATTICE, 25
  IN SPACE LATTICE, 96
SELF COINCIDENCE, 27, 75
SIMPLE UNIT CELL, 22
SINGLE CRYSTAL, *62*
SPACE GROUPS, 135f, *135*
  LATTICE, 66f, *66*
  UNIT CELL OF, 70, 72, 92f
SUBSTITUTIONAL DEFECT, *141*
SYMMETRY, 27f
  ELEMENT, *39*, 82
    CENTRE, *38*, 78
    GLIDE PLANE, *130*
    MIRROR PLANE, *34*, 78
    ROTARY INVERSION AXIS, *79*
    ROTATION AXIS, *28*, 75
    SCREW AXIS, *131*
  OPERATION, *28*, 75
    INVERSION, 37, 78
    REFLECTION, 34, 78
    ROTARY INVERSION, 79,
    ROTATION, 27f, 75f
SYMMETRY, MACROSCOPIC, 75f
  MICROSCOPIC, 129f

TETRAGONAL SYSTEM, 89
  UNIT CELL, 90
TRANSLATION, UNIT, *14*
TRICLINIC SYSTEM, 89
  UNIT CELL, 89
TRIGONAL SYSTEM, 89

UNIT CELL:
  IN PLANE LATTICE, 17f, *17*

AREA OF, 24
CENTRED, 26
SELECTION OF, 25
IN SPACE LATTICE, 71, *72*, 92f
CENTRED, 98f
NUMBER OF ATOMS IN, 192
SELECTION OF, 96
VOLUME OF, 95
UNIT CELL, NON-PRIMITIVE, *23*, 94
PRIMITIVE, *22*, 94

UNIT TRANSLATION, *14*, 70

VACANT ATOM SITE, *140*
VOLUME DEFECT, 145
OF UNIT CELL, 95

X-RAY DIFFRACTION, 180f
X-RAYS, 181

2830